Today's Challenge
Teacher's Guide

Grade 5

enVisionmath® 2.0
SCOTT FORESMAN · ADDISON WESLEY

PEARSON

Glenview, Illinois • Boston, Massachusetts • Chandler, Arizona • Hoboken, New Jersey

ISBN-13:   978-0-328-83710-6
ISBN-10:   0-328-83710-5

1 2 3 4 5 6 7 8 9 10 V0N4 19 18 17 16 15

To the Teacher

Welcome to the Today's Challenge Teacher's Guide.

The *Today's Challenge Teacher's Guide* for **enVision**math**2.0** provides you with detailed teaching support for each day's problem. It allows you to incorporate in-depth teaching of rich problem-solving into your daily instruction.

Within this Teacher's Guide, you will find one page of teaching support for each day's problem. A simple "Before", "During", and "After" method of providing teaching actions will help to guide discussions in either a large-group or a small-group setting. Included in the teaching notes are ample opportunities to differentiate instruction by providing students with extra support or extension.

These teaching pages provide solutions to each of the Today's Challenge problems as well as other features that are described in greater detail on the next page of this Teacher's Guide.

Using This Guide

Topic 1, Day ① ② ③ ④ ⑤

Mars, Mercury, and Venus are planets. Which planet is farthest from Johnson Space Center? Explain how you know.

Approximate Shortest Distance from Johnson Space Center

Location	Distance (in kilometers)
International Space Station (ISS)	350
Kennedy Space Center	1,264
Mars	56,000,000
Mercury	77,300,000
Moon	363,000
Sun	149,600,000
Venus	40,000,000

TEACHING ACTIONS	GUIDING QUESTIONS	DIFFERENTIATED INSTRUCTION
Before 1. Read the problem. 2. Ask guiding questions. 3. Discuss possible solution strategies.	**Make Sense of the Problem** Help students understand the problem: • Which entries in the table are planets? (Mars, Mercury, and Venus) • What are you asked to find? (The planet that is farthest from Johnson Space Center) • What else are you asked to do? (Explain how you know)	
During 4. Observe students. 5. Ask guiding questions as needed. 6. Have students check if their solutions are reasonable.	**Persevere in Solving the Problem** If students need help, ask: • If the planet is the farthest, what does that tell you about the distance? (Sample answer: It will be the greatest number.) • When comparing eight-digit numbers, which digit should you look at first? (The ten millions digit) • Which of the 3 planets has the greatest digit in the ten millions place? (Mercury)	**ELL Support** Provide these sentence frames for students to use in order to complete their answer: _____ is the farthest planet. I know because the distance has the greatest digit in the _____ place. (Mercury, ten millions)
	SOLUTION In the ten millions place, Mercury has the digit 7, Mars has a 5, and Venus has a 4. The greatest of these digits is 7, so Mercury is farthest from Johnson Space Center.	
After 7. Discuss the solution. 8. Discuss how to check if the solution is reasonable. 9. Give the problem an extension as needed.	**Check the Answer** Ask: Which of the 3 planets is closest to Johnson Space Center? How do you know? (Venus, because the digit in the ten millions place of its distance has the least value) Discuss whether students answered the right question. If the Sun is given as the answer, students found the entry in the table with the greatest distance, but not the planet with the greatest distance.	**Extension** Ask: If astronauts could actually fly from Earth to the Sun and back, about how far would they travel in all? Give your answer as a number name. (About three hundred million kilometers; $2 \times 149,600,000 = 299,200,000$)

2 Today's Challenge Teacher's Guide

---

1 Connection to the Topics

Each Topic in **enVision**math**2.0** has a set of 5 Today's Challenge problems. The problems increase in difficulty within a topic and may be assigned anytime during the topic. Today's Challenge reinforces problem-solving strategies and skills using previously taught content.

2 Connection to Science or Other Subject Areas

Each set of problems uses the same data. Familiarity with the information makes students focus on the problem and promotes the kind of thinking needed for success on state assessments.

3 Teaching Actions

Use the Teaching Actions to help students Before, During, and After problem solving.

4 Guiding Questions

Use these questions to guide students through the problem-solving process.

5 Differentiated Instruction

Vocabulary Review, Extra Support, ELL Support, and Extension notes provide you with options for meeting individual student needs.

6 Solutions

A fully developed solution that steps out the process for arriving at the correct answer is provided.

Contents

Topic 1
Understand Place Value

DAY 1 1

DAY 2 2

DAY 3 3

DAY 4 4

DAY 5 5

Topic 2
Add and Subtract Decimals to Hundredths

DAY 1 6

DAY 2 7

DAY 3 8

DAY 4 9

DAY 5 10

Topic 3
Fluently Multiply Multi-Digit Whole Numbers

DAY 1 11

DAY 2 12

DAY 3 13

DAY 4 14

DAY 5 15

Topic 4
Use Models and Strategies to Multiply Decimals

DAY 1 16

DAY 2 17

DAY 3 18

DAY 4 19

DAY 5 20

Contents

Topic 5
Use Models and Strategies to Divide Whole Numbers

DAY 1 21

DAY 2 22

DAY 3 23

DAY 4 24

DAY 5 25

Topic 6
Use Models and Strategies to Divide Decimals

DAY 1 26

DAY 2 27

DAY 3 28

DAY 4 29

DAY 5 30

Topic 7
Use Equivalent Fractions to Add and Subtract Fractions

DAY 1 31

DAY 2 32

DAY 3 33

DAY 4 34

DAY 5 35

Topic 8
Apply Understanding of Multiplication to Multiply Fractions

DAY 1 36

DAY 2 37

DAY 3 38

DAY 4 39

DAY 5 40

Contents

Topic 9
Apply Understanding of Division to Divide Fractions

DAY 1 41

DAY 2 42

DAY 3 43

DAY 4 44

DAY 5 45

Topic 10
Understand Volume Concepts

DAY 1 46

DAY 2 47

DAY 3 48

DAY 4 49

DAY 5 50

Topic 11
Convert Measurements

DAY 1 51

DAY 2 52

DAY 3 53

DAY 4 54

DAY 5 55

Topic 12
Represent and Interpret Data

DAY 1 56

DAY 2 57

DAY 3 58

DAY 4 59

DAY 5 60

Contents

Topic 13
Algebra: Write and Interpret Numerical Expressions

DAY 1 61

DAY 2 62

DAY 3 63

DAY 4 64

DAY 5 65

Topic 14
Graph Points on the Coordinate Plane

DAY 1 66

DAY 2 67

DAY 3 68

DAY 4 69

DAY 5 70

Topic 15
Algebra: Analyze Patterns and Relationships

DAY 1 71

DAY 2 72

DAY 3 73

DAY 4 74

DAY 5 75

Topic 16
Geometric Measurement: Classify Two-Dimensional Figures

DAY 1 76

DAY 2 77

DAY 3 78

DAY 4 79

DAY 5 80

Mars, Mercury and Venus are planets. About how far is Kennedy Space Center from one of the planets? Give your answer as a number name and explain how you know.

Approximate Shortest Distance from Johnson Space Center

Location	Distance (in kilometers)
International Space Station (ISS)	350
Kennedy Space Center	1,264
Mars	56,000,000
Mercury	77,300,000
Moon	363,000
Sun	149,600,000
Venus	40,000,000

TEACHING ACTIONS	GUIDING QUESTIONS	DIFFERENTIATED INSTRUCTION

Before

1. Read the problem.
2. Ask guiding questions.
3. Discuss possible solution strategies.

Make Sense of the Problem

Help students understand the problem:

- What are you asked to find? (The distance from Kennedy Space Center to one of the planets)
- How are you asked to write your answer? (As a number name)

Vocabulary Review

Review what it means to write a number as a *number name*. Ask students to write and say the number name for 123,456,789.

During

4. Observe students.
5. Ask guiding questions as needed.
6. Have students check if their solutions are reasonable.

Persevere in Solving the Problem

If students need help, ask:

- What is the distance from Venus to Johnson Space Center? (40,000,000 km) What is the value of the 4 in that number? (40 million)
- How does the distance between the space centers compare to the distance to one of the planets? (Sample answer: The distance from either space center to any of the planets is much greater than the distance between the space centers.)

SOLUTION Sample answer: From Mercury, about seventy-seven million, three hundred thousand kilometers. The space centers are only about 1,200 km apart, so the distance from either center to any one of the planets will be about the same. I can use the distance in the table.

ELL Support

Make sure students understand the differences between the meanings of the math words *hundred, thousand,* and *million.* Point out that the zeros in each number help you know which math word to coordinate with each numeral.

After

7. Discuss the solution.
8. Discuss how to check if the solution is reasonable.
9. Give the problem an extension as needed.

Check the Answer

Ask: Why is it important to look at place value when answering this question? (Sample answer: You need to know if the number is seventy-seven thousand or seventy-seven million.)

To check if their solutions are reasonable, ask students to see whether the word *million* appears in their answer. Students should find that it does because the distances to all planets are in millions of kilometers.

Extension

Say: Alison flew round-trip between Johnson and Kennedy Space Centers. How far did she fly? Give your answer in word form. (Two thousand, five hundred twenty-eight kilometers)

Today's Challenge Teacher's Guide

Mars, Mercury, and Venus are planets. Which planet is farthest from Johnson Space Center? Explain how you know.

Approximate Shortest Distance from Johnson Space Center

Location	Distance (in kilometers)
International Space Station (ISS)	350
Kennedy Space Center	1,264
Mars	56,000,000
Mercury	77,300,000
Moon	363,000
Sun	149,600,000
Venus	40,000,000

TEACHING ACTIONS	GUIDING QUESTIONS	DIFFERENTIATED INSTRUCTION

Before

1. Read the problem.
2. Ask guiding questions.
3. Discuss possible solution strategies.

Make Sense of the Problem

Help students understand the problem:

- Which entries in the table are planets? (Mars, Mercury, and Venus)
- What are you asked to find? (The planet that is farthest from Johnson Space Center)
- What else are you asked to do? (Explain how you know)

During

4. Observe students.
5. Ask guiding questions as needed.
6. Have students check if their solutions are reasonable.

Persevere in Solving the Problem

If students need help, ask:

- If the planet is the farthest, what does that tell you about the distance? (Sample answer: It will be the greatest number.)
- When comparing eight-digit numbers, which digit should you look at first? (The ten millions digit)
- Which of the 3 planets has the greatest digit in the ten millions place? (Mercury)

SOLUTION In the ten millions place, Mercury has the digit 7, Mars has a 5, and Venus has a 4. The greatest of these digits is 7, so Mercury is farthest from Johnson Space Center.

ELL Support

Provide these sentence frames for students to use in order to complete their answer: _____ is the farthest planet. I know because the distance has the greatest digit in the _____ place. (Mercury, ten millions)

After

7. Discuss the solution.
8. Discuss how to check if the solution is reasonable.
9. Give the problem an extension as needed.

Check the Answer

Ask: Which of the 3 planets is closest to Johnson Space Center? How do you know? (Venus, because the digit in the ten millions place of its distance has the least value)

Discuss whether students answered the right question. If the Sun is given as the answer, students found the entry in the table with the greatest distance, but not the planet with the greatest distance.

Extension

Ask: If astronauts could actually fly from Earth to the Sun and back, about how far would they travel in all? Give your answer as a number name. (About three hundred million kilometers; $2 \times 149,600,000 = 299,200,000$)

What is the value of each 7 in the distance to Mercury? How are the values related? Explain how you know.

Approximate Shortest Distance from Johnson Space Center

Location	Distance (in kilometers)
International Space Station (ISS)	350
Kennedy Space Center	1,264
Mars	56,000,000
Mercury	77,300,000
Moon	363,000
Sun	149,600,000
Venus	40,000,000

TEACHING ACTIONS	GUIDING QUESTIONS	DIFFERENTIATED INSTRUCTION

Before

1. Read the problem.
2. Ask guiding questions.
3. Discuss possible solution strategies.

Make Sense of the Problem

Help students understand the problem:

- What are you asked to find first? (The value of each 7 in the distance to Mercury)
- What are you asked to do next? (Explain how the values are related.)

Vocabulary Review

Review the meaning of the term *value*. Remind students that the word is part of the term *place value*, which relates to the location of a digit in a number.

During

4. Observe students.
5. Ask guiding questions as needed.
6. Have students check if their solutions are reasonable.

Persevere in Solving the Problem

If students need help, ask:

- About how many kilometers is Mercury from the Johnson Space Center? (About 77,300,000 km)
- What is the value of each 7 in the distance? (70 million; 7 million) How are these values related? (Sample answer: 70 million is 10 times as great as 7 million.)

SOLUTION The values of the 7s in 77,300,00 are 70 million and 7 million; Sample answer: 70,000,000 is 10 times as great as 7,000,000 because each place value is 10 times as great as the place value to its right.

Extra Support

If students have trouble finding the solution, encourage them to write the distance in a place-value chart. Have them look at the number of places between the ten millions and the millions.

After

7. Discuss the solution.
8. Discuss how to check if the solution is reasonable.
9. Give the problem an extension as needed.

Check the Answer

Ask: How can you check that your answer is correct? (I know that 70 is 10 times 7, so I know that 70 million is 10 times 7 million.)

To check if their solutions are reasonable, ask students what numbers are 10 times, 100 times, and 1,000 times as great as 7 (70; 700; 7,000). They should see that 70,000,000 is 10 times as great as 7,000,000.

Extension

Ask: About how many times as far is it to the Sun as it is to Mercury? How do you know? (About twice; Sample answer: I can use compatible numbers to estimate: 75,000,000 × 2 = 150,000,000)

Today's Challenge Teacher's Guide

How much farther from Johnson Space Center is Kennedy Space Center than the International Space Station? Write an equation to solve.

Approximate Shortest Distance from Johnson Space Center

Location	Distance (in kilometers)
International Space Station (ISS)	350
Kennedy Space Center	1,264
Mars	56,000,000
Mercury	77,300,000
Moon	363,000
Sun	149,600,000
Venus	40,000,000

TEACHING ACTIONS	GUIDING QUESTIONS	DIFFERENTIATED INSTRUCTION

Before

1. Read the problem.
2. Ask guiding questions.
3. Discuss possible solution strategies.

Make Sense of the Problem

Help students understand the problem:

- What information do you need to find in the table? (The distance to the Kennedy Space Center and the distance to the International Space Station)
- What are you asked to write? (An equation)

Vocabulary Review

Review the meaning of the term *equation*. As a class, write a simple equation with a variable, and then make up a story that the equation models.

During

4. Observe students.
5. Ask guiding questions as needed.
6. Have students check if their solutions are reasonable.

Persevere in Solving the Problem

If students need help, ask:

- What words tell you the operation to use? (*How much farther*) Which operation will you use? (Subtraction)
- What will you subtract? (Sample answer: The distance to the International Space Station from the distance to Kennedy Space Center)

SOLUTION It is 1,264 km to Kennedy Space Center and 350 km to the International Space Station. $n = 1,264 - 350$, so $n = 914$; the difference is 914 km.

Extra Support

If students have trouble finding the solution, suggest that they draw a picture. Have them draw a point for the ISS above the points for the space centers. Then have them label the distance from Johnson Space Center to each.

After

7. Discuss the solution.
8. Discuss how to check if the solution is reasonable.
9. Give the problem an extension as needed.

Check the Answer

Ask: Should the answer be greater than or less than 1,264? Why? (Less than; The difference between two numbers must be less than the greater number.)

Discuss whether students answered the right question. Students who answer 1,614 found the sum of the distances instead of the difference between them.

Extension

Say: On Friday, Ty drove 419 km. The next day, he continued to his destination. He drove a total of 1,276 km. Write and solve an equation to find the distance he drove the second day. (Sample answer: $1,276 - d = 419$; $d = 857$ km)

To the nearest whole number, how many times farther from Johnson Space Center is Kennedy Space Center than the International Space Station? Tell how to use an equation to solve.

Approximate Shortest Distance from Johnson Space Center

Location	Distance (in kilometers)
International Space Station (ISS)	350
Kennedy Space Center	1,264
Mars	56,000,000
Mercury	77,300,000
Moon	363,000
Sun	149,600,000
Venus	40,000,000

TEACHING ACTIONS	GUIDING QUESTIONS	DIFFERENTIATED INSTRUCTION

Before

1. Read the problem.
2. Ask guiding questions.
3. Discuss possible solution strategies.

Make Sense of the Problem

Help students understand the problem:

- What are you asked to find? (How many times farther from Johnson Space Center is Kennedy Space Center than the International Space Station)
- How are you asked to round the answer? (To the nearest whole number)

During

4. Observe students.
5. Ask guiding questions as needed.
6. Have students check if their solutions are reasonable.

Persevere in Solving the Problem

If students need help, ask:

- What question can you ask to help write the equation? (Sample answer: The distance to Kennedy Space Station from Johnson Space Center is how many times as far as the distance to the International Space Station from Johnson Space Center?)
- How can you estimate to find the answer? (Sample answer: Try 2 times and multiply 2×350. If the product is not close enough to 1,264, try 3 times and 4 times and multiply 3×350 and 4×350.)

> **SOLUTION** Kennedy Space Center is about 4 times farther. Sample answer: The equation is $n \times 350 = 1,264$. Using compatible numbers, the estimated solution is 4. I found $4 \times 350 = 1,400$. This product is close to 1,264.

Extra Support

If students have trouble finding the solution, have them work in small groups. In their groups, have them find 2×350, 3×350, 4×350, and 5×350. Then have them see which product is closest to 1,264.

After

7. Discuss the solution.
8. Discuss how to check if the solution is reasonable.
9. Give the problem an extension as needed.

Check the Answer

Ask: When estimating, is it easier to multiply 350 by each number or to divide 1,264 by each number? Why? (Multiply 350; Sample answer: 350 is a multiple of 10 that is easy to multiply with.)

Discuss with students how they found their solutions. Students who answer incorrectly have either not calculated correctly, not used the correct numbers, or not rounded their answer correctly.

Extension

Ask: About how many times farther is the Sun from Earth than the Moon from Earth? How did you find the answer? (Sample answer: About 375 times farther; I rounded the distances to 150,000,000 for the Sun and 400,000 for the Moon and then divided; $150,000,000 \div 400,000 = 375$.)

Today's Challenge Teacher's Guide

Write the part of the daily value of one nutrient, besides copper, in expanded form.

The Nutrition of Shrimp

Nutrient	Part of Daily Value in 113.4 g of Shrimp
Copper	0.11
Iron	0.194
Protein	0.474
Vitamin B3	0.147
Vitamin B12	0.281
Zinc	0.118

TEACHING ACTIONS	GUIDING QUESTIONS	DIFFERENTIATED INSTRUCTION

Before

1. Read the problem.
2. Ask guiding questions.
3. Discuss possible solution strategies.

Make Sense of the Problem

Help students understand the problem:

- What are you asked to write? (The part of the daily value of one nutrient)
- Which nutrient can you choose? (Any nutrient other than copper)
- In what form are you asked to write the answer? (In expanded form)

Vocabulary Review

Review the term *expanded form*. Ask students for their definitions or explanations of the same term.

During

4. Observe students.
5. Ask guiding questions as needed.
6. Have students check if their solutions are reasonable.

Persevere in Solving the Problem

If students need help, ask:

- What does expanded form show? (Sample answer: The value of each digit as addends)
- What is the first number you will write in expanded form? (The value of the digit in the tenths place)
- What is the second number you will write? (The value of the digit in the hundredths place)

SOLUTION Sample answer: Iron is 0.194 of the daily value: $0.194 = 0.1 + 0.09 + 0.004$.

ELL Support

Make sure students understand the word *nutrient*. Tell students that *nutrient* comes from a Latin word meaning "to feed." Ask for other words that might come from the same Latin word. (Sample answer: *Nutritious, nourishment*)

After

7. Discuss the solution.
8. Discuss how to check if the solution is reasonable.
9. Give the problem an extension as needed.

Check the Answer

Ask: Why is it important to look at the place value of each digit in the number? (Sample answer: Place value shows you what value to write for each digit in expanded form.)

To check if their solutions are reasonable, ask students to take their answer written in expanded form and add the decimals. For example, have them add $0.1 + 0.09 + 0.004$. Students should arrive at the original number.

Extension

Say: The amount of shrimp shown in the table can be considered 1 serving. Jill ate 2 servings of shrimp. What part of the daily value of vitamin B12 did she receive? Write your answer in expanded form. ($0.281 \times 2 = 0.562$; $0.562 = 0.5 + 0.06 + 0.002$)

List the nutrients in order from the one with the least part of daily value to the one with the greatest part of daily value.

The Nutrition of Shrimp

Nutrient	Part of Daily Value in 113.4 g of Shrimp
Copper	0.11
Iron	0.194
Protein	0.474
Vitamin B3	0.147
Vitamin B12	0.281
Zinc	0.118

TEACHING ACTIONS	GUIDING QUESTIONS	DIFFERENTIATED INSTRUCTION

Before

1. Read the problem.
2. Ask guiding questions.
3. Discuss possible solution strategies.

Make Sense of the Problem

Help students understand the problem:

- How are you asked to order the nutrients? (From the one with the least part of daily value to the one with the greatest part of daily value)
- Are you asked to list the names of the nutrients or the values? (The names of the nutrients)

Vocabulary Review

Review the meaning of the term *value*. Ask students for the value of the 7 in the number 319,405.9702. (7 hundredths)

During

4. Observe students.
5. Ask guiding questions as needed.
6. Have students check if their solutions are reasonable.

Persevere in Solving the Problem

If students need help, ask:

- Will you list the nutrients beginning with the least or greatest number? (Least)
- When comparing decimals less than one, what digit do you compare first? (The digit in the tenths place)
- If 2 numbers have the same digit in the tenths place, what digit do you compare next? (The digit in the hundredths place)

SOLUTION The nutrients listed in order from least to greatest daily value: copper (0.11), zinc (0.118), vitamin B3 (0.147), iron (0.194), vitamin B12 (0.281), protein (0.474)

Extra Support

If students have trouble finding the solution, encourage them to use a place-value chart. Have students learn the name of each place to the right of the decimal point and then begin comparing digits in the tenths place.

After

7. Discuss the solution.
8. Discuss how to check if the solution is reasonable.
9. Give the problem an extension as needed.

Check the Answer

Ask: What do you know about the last number in the list? (Sample answer: It is the greatest number in the list.)

Discuss whether students answered the right question. If *protein* is given as the first nutrient in the answer, students may have listed the nutrients in order from greatest to least daily value instead of from least to greatest daily value.

Extension

Say: Name 3 numbers that are between 0.00197 and 0.00203. (Sample answer: 0.00199, 0.002, and 0.00201)

How much more of the part of the daily value of iron than zinc are in 113.4 grams of shrimp? Explain how to find the answer.

The Nutrition of Shrimp

Nutrient	Part of Daily Value in 113.4 g of Shrimp
Copper	0.11
Iron	0.194
Protein	0.474
Vitamin B3	0.147
Vitamin B12	0.281
Zinc	0.118

TEACHING ACTIONS	GUIDING QUESTIONS	DIFFERENTIATED INSTRUCTION

Before

1. Read the problem.
2. Ask guiding questions.
3. Discuss possible solution strategies.

Make Sense of the Problem

Help students understand the problem:

- Which daily values are you asked to compare? (The daily values of iron and zinc)
- What else are you asked to do? (Explain how to find the answer)

During

4. Observe students.
5. Ask guiding questions as needed.
6. Have students check if their solutions are reasonable.

Persevere in Solving the Problem

If students need help, ask:

- What words tell you which operation to use? (*How much more*)
- Which operation should you use? (Subtraction)
- Which daily value will you subtract from which? (Subtract the daily value for zinc from the daily value for iron)

SOLUTION The difference between the daily values for iron and zinc can be found using the equation: $0.194 - 0.118 = 0.076$. The part of the daily value of iron is 0.076 greater than the part of the daily value of zinc in 113.4 g of shrimp.

ELL Support

For students who need extra language support, read the word problem together. Encourage them to rephrase the problem. They might rephrase it as: How much greater is 0.194 than 0.118?

After

7. Discuss the solution.
8. Discuss how to check if their solution is reasonable.
9. Give the problem an extension as needed.

Check the Answer

Ask: How do you make sure you use the correct place value in your answer? (Sample answer: Arrange the numbers vertically with the decimal points aligned and then subtract, starting with the digits in the thousandths place.)

Discuss whether students answered the right question. If 0.312 is given for the answer, students found the sum of the amounts instead of finding the difference.

Extension

Ask: How much greater are the values of vitamin B3 and vitamin B12 combined than the values of iron and zinc combined? (0.116; $0.428 - 0.312 = 0.116$)

Which two nutrients have the same part of daily value when rounded to the nearest tenth? Explain your answer.

The Nutrition of Shrimp

Nutrient	Part of Daily Value in 113.4 g of Shrimp
Copper	0.11
Iron	0.194
Protein	0.474
Vitamin B3	0.147
Vitamin B12	0.281
Zinc	0.118

TEACHING ACTIONS	GUIDING QUESTIONS	DIFFERENTIATED INSTRUCTION

Before

1. Read the problem.
2. Ask guiding questions.
3. Discuss possible solution strategies.

Make Sense of the Problem

Help students understand the problem:

- What are you asked to find? (2 nutrients that have the same part of daily value when rounded to the nearest tenth)
- What else are you asked to do? (Explain the answer)

Vocabulary Review

Review the term *thousandths*. Ask: What digit is in the thousandths place in the number 279,041.658? (8)

During

4. Observe students.
5. Ask guiding questions as needed.
6. Have students check if their solutions are reasonable.

Persevere in Solving the Problem

If students need help, ask:

- What is the first step to solve this problem? (Round each number to the nearest tenth)
- What digit do you look at when rounding to the nearest tenth? (Hundredths)
- What is the value for iron, 0.194, rounded to the nearest tenth? (0.2)

SOLUTION Copper, vitamin B3, and zinc all have 0.1 part of daily value when rounded to the nearest tenth. Students can name any 2 of these.

ELL Support

Make sure all students understand the difference between *ten* and *tenth* and between *hundred* and *hundredth*. Have them practice rounding numbers to the nearest ten, tenth, hundred, and hundredth.

After

7. Discuss the solution.
8. Discuss how to check if the solution is reasonable.
9. Give the problem an extension as needed.

Check the Answer

Ask: Is there more than one correct answer to this question? How do you know? (Yes; More than 2 of the numbers round to 0.1.)

To check if their solutions are reasonable, ask students to find the numbers in the table that do NOT round to 0.1. They should respond that iron, protein, and vitamin B12 do not round to 0.1 and should not appear in their answer.

Extension

Say: 5 runners had finishing times of 9.194, 9.208, 9.115, 9.267, and 9.214 seconds. Which times are the same when rounded to the nearest hundredth? (9.208 and 9.214 both round to 9.21.)

Today's Challenge Teacher's Guide

When rounded to the nearest tenth, which two nutrients have about the same combined part of the daily value as protein? Explain your answer.

The Nutrition of Shrimp

Nutrient	Part of Daily Value in 113.4 g of Shrimp
Copper	0.11
Iron	0.194
Protein	0.474
Vitamin B3	0.147
Vitamin B12	0.281
Zinc	0.118

TEACHING ACTIONS	GUIDING QUESTIONS	DIFFERENTIATED INSTRUCTION

Before

1. Read the problem.
2. Ask guiding questions.
3. Discuss possible solution strategies.

Make Sense of the Problem

Help students understand the problem:

- What are you asked to find? (The 2 nutrients that have about the same combined part of the daily value as protein)
- How are you asked to round the numbers? (To the nearest tenth)

During

4. Observe students.
5. Ask guiding questions as needed.
6. Have students check if their solutions are reasonable.

Persevere in Solving the Problem

If students need help, ask:

- What is the value for protein? (0.474) What is this number rounded to the nearest tenth? (0.5)
- What do you need to find? (The nutrients whose combined rounded values equal 0.5)
- What nutrient might you try first? Why? (Vitamin B12, because it has one of the largest values)

SOLUTION Protein rounds to 0.5. Vitamin B12 rounds to 0.3, and iron rounds to 0.2. Then I added 0.3 + 0.2 = 0.5. So the 2 nutrients that have about the same combined part of the daily value as protein are vitamin B12 and iron.

Extra Support

If students have trouble finding the solution, suggest that they write the values from the tables and the rounded values on index cards. Then have students rearrange the cards to try to make 0.5.

After

7. Discuss the solution.
8. Discuss how to check if the solution is reasonable.
9. Give the problem an extension as needed.

Check the Answer

Ask: Why is it important to round the value for protein to the nearest tenth? (Sample answer: You need to know the rounded part of the daily value of protein to be able to find 2 nutrients whose combined rounded value is estimated to be about the same.)

To check if their solutions are reasonable, ask students to add the exact values for the nutrients they found. Students should find that the exact sum of the 2 values is very close to the exact value for protein.

Extension

Ask: Which 3 nutrients have a combined part of the daily value of exactly 0.949? (Iron, protein, and vitamin B12)

Today's Challenge Teacher's Guide

In 10 minutes, how many times does a horse's heart beat? Write an equation to solve.

Animal	Heartbeats per Minute
Bat	750
Cat	150
Chicken	275
Dog (medium size)	90
Elephant	30
Horse	44
Hamster	450
Monkey	192
Pig	70
Rabbit	205
Whale (large size)	22

TEACHING ACTIONS	GUIDING QUESTIONS	DIFFERENTIATED INSTRUCTION
Before 1. Read the problem. 2. Ask guiding questions. 3. Discuss possible solution strategies.	**Make Sense of the Problem** Help students understand the problem: • What are you asked to find? (How many times a horse's heart beats in 10 minutes) • What are you asked to do in order to solve the problem? (Write an equation.)	**Vocabulary Review** Review the term *equation*. Remind students that in an equation, they use an equal sign, a symbol showing that the value on the left side of the sign is the same as the value on the right side.
During 4. Observe students. 5. Ask guiding questions as needed. 6. Have students check if their solutions are reasonable.	**Persevere in Solving the Problem** If students need help, ask: • What do you know about a horse's heartbeat from the table? (In 1 minute, a horse's heart beats 44 times.) • Which operation can you use to solve the problem? Explain. (Sample answer: I can use multiplication. If the horse's heart beats 44 times in 1 minute, then I can multiply 44 by 10 to find how many times it beats in 10 minutes.) • What equation can you write to solve the problem? ($10 \times 44 = n$)	**Extra Support** Write several one-step equations on the board. Have students solve each equation, making sure that the value on the left side of the equal sign is the same as the value on the right side.
	SOLUTION A horse's heart beats 440 times in 10 minutes; Sample equation: $10 \times 44 = n$, so $n = 440$.	
After 7. Discuss the solution. 8. Discuss how to check if the solution is reasonable. 9. Give the problem an extension as needed.	**Check the Answer** Ask: Can you use mental math to solve your equation? Explain your answer. (Yes; Sample answer: Because I am asked to find how many times the horse's heart beats in 10 minutes, I can multiply 44 by 1 ten and get 44 tens. I know that 44 tens is 440. To check if their solutions are reasonable, ask students to use division to check their answer. Ask: What is the inverse operation of multiplication? (Division) How can you use division to check your answer? (I can divide 440 by 10 to get 44.)	**Extension** Ask: In 20 minutes, how many times does a horse's heart beat? Solve the problem using mental math and explain how you found your answer. (880 beats in 20 minutes; Sample answer: I multiplied 44 by 2 tens and got 88 tens. I know that 88 tens is 880.

In 10 minutes, how many more times does a chicken's heart beat than a whale's heart? Describe 2 different ways to find the answer.

Animal	Heartbeats per Minute
Bat	750
Cat	150
Chicken	275
Dog (medium size)	90
Elephant	30
Horse	44
Hamster	450
Monkey	192
Pig	70
Rabbit	205
Whale (large size)	22

TEACHING ACTIONS	GUIDING QUESTIONS	DIFFERENTIATED INSTRUCTION

Before

1. Read the problem.
2. Ask guiding questions.
3. Discuss possible solution strategies.

Make Sense of the Problem

Help students understand the problem:

- How many times does a chicken's heart beat in a minute? (275) A whale's heart? (22)
- What are you asked to find? (How many more times a chicken's heart beats than a whale's heart in 10 minutes)

Vocabulary Review

Ask students to name the property that allows them to solve the problem two different ways. (Distributive Property)

During

4. Observe students.
5. Ask guiding questions as needed.
6. Have students check if their solutions are reasonable.

Persevere in Solving the Problem

If students need help, ask:

- Which operations would you use to solve the problem? (Multiplication and subtraction)
- How can the Distributive Property help you solve the problem two different ways? (Sample answer: I can multiply first and then subtract, or vice versa.)

SOLUTION A chicken's heart beats $10 \times 275 = 2,750$ times in 10 minutes. A whale's heart beats $10 \times 22 = 220$ beats in 10 minutes. $2,750 - 220 = 2,530$. A different way to solve: A chicken's heart beats $275 - 22 = 253$ more times each minute than a whale's heart beats, so it beats $10 \times 253 = 2,530$ more times in 10 minutes.

Extra Support

To help students keep track of their steps, ask them to write out a plan before they solve the problem. (Solution 1: Multiply 10×275, multiply 10×22, and subtract the products; Solution 2: Subtract $275 - 22$ and multiply the difference by 10)

After

7. Discuss the solution.
8. Discuss how to check if the solution is reasonable.
9. Give the problem an extension as needed.

Check the Answer

Ask: Can you multiply by 10 using mental math? Explain. (Yes; Sample answer: The product of a whole number and 10 is the number with a 0 written to its right in the ones place.)

Say: A student says, "A whale's heart beats 480 more times in 10 minutes than a chicken's heart." Is this reasonable? Explain. (No; Sample answer: A chicken's heart beats more than a whale's heart in one minute, so it wouldn't make sense for a whale's heart to beat more than a chicken's heart in 10 minutes.)

Extension

Ask: Which way do you prefer to solve the problem? Explain. (Sample answer: I prefer to subtract first. When you subtract first, the numbers are smaller and easier to multiply, and I can solve the problem in 2 steps instead of 3.)

Today's Challenge Teacher's Guide

Which animal has a heart rate that is 5 times that of a different animal? Name both animals. Find more animals with a heart rate 5 times that of a different animal.

Animal	Heartbeats per Minute
Bat	750
Cat	150
Chicken	275
Dog (medium size)	90
Elephant	30
Horse	44
Hamster	450
Monkey	192
Pig	70
Rabbit	205
Whale (large size)	22

TEACHING ACTIONS	GUIDING QUESTIONS	DIFFERENTIATED INSTRUCTION

Before

1. Read the problem.
2. Ask guiding questions.
3. Discuss possible solution strategies.

Make Sense of the Problem

Help students understand the problem:

- What are you asked to do? (Find animals with a heart rate 5 times that of another listed animal)
- What is the relationship between the heart rates? (One heart rate is 5 times as fast as the other.)

Vocabulary Review

Have students complete the following sentence frame: The term *5 times* means _____ by 5. (multiply)

During

4. Observe students.
5. Ask guiding questions as needed.
6. Have students check if their solutions are reasonable.

Persevere in Solving the Problem

If students need help, ask:

- What information do you have to use? (The heartbeats per minute of different animals)
- How would you choose a pair of animals to use? (Sample answer: I would start with the animal with the fewest heartbeats per minute. Then I would multiply its heart rate by 5 to see if the product is equal to another animal's heart rate.)

ELL Support

Have students show they understand the meaning of *5 times* by creating a model with place-value blocks for the correct equation.

> **SOLUTION** Sample answers: A cat's heart rate is 5 times an elephant's heart rate ($30 \times 5 = 150$). A hamster's heart rate is 5 times a medium-sized dog's heart rate ($90 \times 5 = 450$). A bat's heart rate is 5 times a cat's heart rate ($150 \times 5 = 750$).

After

7. Discuss the solution.
8. Discuss how to check if the solution is reasonable.
9. Give the problem an extension as needed.

Check the Answer

Say: You know that a bat's heart rate is 5 times a cat's heart rate. Explain why you would not multiply a monkey's heart rate by 5 to find another possible answer. (750 is the greatest number of heartbeats listed, and $5 \times 192 = 960$, which is greater than 750.)

Say: A student thinks a rabbit's heart rate is 5 times a whale's heart rate. Is this reasonable? Explain. (No; Sample answer: I know that $20 \times 5 = 100$, so 22×5 cannot be 205.)

Extension

Say: Explain why the following sentence is not correct: A cat's heart rate is 5 times a bat's heart rate. (Sample answer: 5 times a bat's heart rate is 5×750, which is greater than 150.)

Today's Challenge Teacher's Guide

A canary has a heart rate of about 17 beats per second. How does the canary's heart rate compare to the bat's heart rate? Explain. (Remember, there are 60 seconds in a minute.)

Animal	Heartbeats per Minute
Bat	750
Cat	150
Chicken	275
Dog (medium size)	90
Elephant	30
Horse	44
Hamster	450
Monkey	192
Pig	70
Rabbit	205
Whale (large size)	22

TEACHING ACTIONS	GUIDING QUESTIONS	DIFFERENTIATED INSTRUCTION

Before

1. Read the problem.
2. Ask guiding questions.
3. Discuss possible solution strategies.

Make Sense of the Problem

Help students understand the problem:

- What are you asked to do? (Find how the canary's heart rate compares to the bat's heart rate.)
- How is the canary's heartbeat given? (Beats per second) How is the bat's heartbeat given? (Beats per minute)

Vocabulary Review

Have students complete the following sentence frame: There are 60 _____ in 1 *minute*. (seconds)

During

4. Observe students.
5. Ask guiding questions as needed.
6. Have students check if their solutions are reasonable.

Persevere in Solving the Problem

If students need help, ask:

- How can you find the number of heart beats in 1 minute for a canary? (Multiply the number of heartbeats in 1 second for a canary by 60, the number of seconds in a minute.)
- How can you compare the number of heartbeats per minute for the canary to the number of heartbeats per minute for the bat? (Sample answer: Subtract to find the difference.)

SOLUTION A canary's heart beats $17 \times 60 = 1{,}020$ times in 1 minute. I can subtract the number of heartbeats per minute for the bat from the number of heartbeats per minute for the canary to compare. A canary's heart beats about $1{,}020 - 750 = 270$ more times per minute than a bat's heart beats.

ELL Support

Help students understand that they need to convert the canary's heart beats per second to beats per minute. Explain that when comparing, students need to compare the same units, in this case heartbeats per minute.

After

7. Discuss the solution.
8. Discuss how to check if the solution is reasonable.
9. Give the problem an extension as needed.

Check the Answer

Ask: How many times does the canary's heart beat beat in 10 seconds? (170 times) How can you use this information to check part of your answer? (Sample answer: I can multiply 170 by 6 to find how many times the canary's heart beats in 1 minute.)

Ask: How can you check if your comparison is reasonable? (Sample answer: I can use the inverse operation to check my comparisons. Since I found that $1{,}020 - 750 = 270$, I can add to find $270 + 750 = 1{,}020$.)

Extension

Say: Is it true that a canary's heart rate per minute is the same as a rabbit's heart rate per 10 minutes? Explain (No; A canary's heart beats 1,020 times per minute and a rabbit's heart beats $10 \times 205 = 2{,}050$ times in 10 minutes.)

Today's Challenge Teacher's Guide

For each animal listed below, find the number of times the animal's heart beats in 1 hour. (Remember, there are 60 minutes in an hour.)

Dog   Elephant   Horse   Pig   Whale

How many times does your heart beat in an hour? Check your pulse for a minute, or use the average human heart rate of 72 beats per minute.

Animal	Heartbeats per Minute
Bat	750
Cat	150
Chicken	275
Dog (medium size)	90
Elephant	30
Horse	44
Hamster	450
Monkey	192
Pig	70
Rabbit	205
Whale (large size)	22

TEACHING ACTIONS	GUIDING QUESTIONS	DIFFERENTIATED INSTRUCTION
Before 1. Read the problem. 2. Ask guiding questions. 3. Discuss possible solution strategies.	**Make Sense of the Problem** Help students understand the problem: • How many times does a dog's heart beat in 1 minute? (90) An elephant's? (30) A horse's? (44) A pig's? (70) A whale's? (22) • What are you asked to find for each animal listed? (The number of times its heart beats in 1 hour) For you? (The number of times my heart beats in 1 hour)	
During 4. Observe students. 5. Ask guiding questions as needed. 6. Have students check if their solutions are reasonable.	**Persevere in Solving the Problem** If students need help, ask: • What would you do to the given heart rates to find the number of heartbeats in 1 hour? Explain. (Multiply each heart rate by 60 because there are 60 minutes in 1 hour) • How might a drawing help you multiply? (Sample answer: I can draw an array. I would separate each factor into tens and ones and then add the partial products.) **SOLUTION** Multiply the number of each animal's heartbeats per minute by 60 to find the rate per hour. Dog: 5,400 times; elephant: 1,800 times; horse: 2,640 times; pig: 4,200 times; whale: 1,320 times; Sample answer: Human (at 72 beats per minute): 4,320 times	**Extra Support** To help students multiply multiples of 10, have them use a pattern. For example, to find 90×60: $9 \times 6 = 54$ $9 \times 60 = 540$ $90 \times 60 = 5,400$
After 7. Discuss the solution. 8. Discuss how to check if the solution is reasonable. 9. Give the problem an extension as needed.	**Check the Answer** Ask: When can you multiply mentally? (Sample answer: When I multiply multiples of 10) What is a way you can check your answer? (Sample answer: I can switch the order of the factors.) Say: In this problem you assume an animal's heart beats the same number of beats every minute for an hour. Do you think this is always true? (Sample answer: No; A heart rate can go up or down depending on what an animal is doing.)	**Extension** Ask: How would you find the number of heartbeats in a day for the given animals? (Sample answer: I would take the number of heartbeats I found for 1 hour and multiply it by 24 because there are 24 hours in a day.)

Today's Challenge Teacher's Guide

On which planets would you weigh more than you do on Earth? How do you know?

Planet	Weight Relative to Earth
Mercury	0.38
Venus	0.90
Earth	1.00
Mars	0.38
Jupiter	2.36
Saturn	0.92
Uranus	0.89
Neptune	1.13

TEACHING ACTIONS	GUIDING QUESTIONS	DIFFERENTIATED INSTRUCTION

Before

1. Read the problem.
2. Ask guiding questions.
3. Discuss possible solution strategies.

Make Sense of the Problem

Help students understand the problem:

- What are you asked to find? (The planets on which you would weigh more than you do on Earth)
- What information are you given? (A table of planets and weights relative to Earth)

Vocabulary Review

Explain that the word *relative* as it is used in the table means *compared to*. The numerical data are used to compare weights of various objects on Earth to the other planets.

During

4. Observe students.
5. Ask guiding questions as needed.
6. Have students check if their solutions are reasonable.

Persevere in Solving the Problem

If students need help, ask:

- If you weighed more on another planet, would the weight relative to Earth be greater than or less than 1? (Greater than 1)
- When comparing the numbers in the table to 1, which digit will you look at first? (The ones digit)
- Which numbers in the table are greater than 1? (2.36 and 1.13)

SOLUTION You would weigh more on Jupiter and Neptune than you do on Earth. $2.36 > 1.00$ and $1.13 > 1.00$

ELL Support

Help students understand the difference between *weight* and *weigh*. Explain that *weight*, a noun, is a measurement of how heavy a person or object is. *Weigh*, a verb, means "to measure the weight of a person or object." The past tense is *weighed*.

After

7. Discuss the solution.
8. Discuss how to check if the solution is reasonable.
9. Give the problem an extension as needed.

Check the Answer

Say: Look at the numbers in the table that are less than 1. What digit is in the ones place? (0)

Ask: On how many planets would you weigh less than you do on Earth? How can you use this to check your answer? (Sample answer: I would weigh less on 5 planets than I do on Earth. I can add this number to the number of planets in my original solution and then add 1 more for Earth: $5 + 2 + 1 = 8$ planets in all, so I have considered all the planets.)

Extension

Ask: Would an object weigh more on Mars or on Mercury? Explain. (The object would weigh the same because an object's weight relative to Earth is the same on both planets.)

Today's Challenge Teacher's Guide

Kalinda took a bag of apples on her trip to Mars. The apples weighed 5 pounds on Earth. How much will the bag of apples weigh on Mars? Write and solve an equation.

Planet	Weight Relative to Earth
Mercury	0.38
Venus	0.90
Earth	1.00
Mars	0.38
Jupiter	2.36
Saturn	0.92
Uranus	0.89
Neptune	1.13

TEACHING ACTIONS	GUIDING QUESTIONS	DIFFERENTIATED INSTRUCTION

Before

1. Read the problem.
2. Ask guiding questions.
3. Discuss possible solution strategies.

Make Sense of the Problem

Help students understand the problem:

- How much did the bag of apples weigh on Earth? (5 pounds)
- What are you asked to find? (How much the bag of apples will weigh on Mars)
- What else are you asked to do? (Write and solve an equation.)

Vocabulary Review

Review the meaning of *pound*. Tell students that its abbreviation is *lb*. Adding an *s* to make the abbreviation plural is not needed. Write *10 lb* and read it aloud as a class as *ten pounds*.

During

4. Observe students.
5. Ask guiding questions as needed.
6. Have students check if their solutions are reasonable.

Persevere in Solving the Problem

If students need help, ask:

- How can you find the weight of the bag of apples on Mars? (Multiply 5 pounds by 0.38.)
- What equation can you write to find the weight of the apples on Mars? (Sample answer: $5 \times 0.38 = n$)

SOLUTION The apples will weigh 1.9 pounds on Mars; Sample answer: 5 pounds of apples on Earth $\times$ 0.38 = n pounds of apples on Mars; $n = 1.9$ lb

ELL Support

Students whose first language is not English may not be familiar with *pound* as a unit of measurement. Provide examples such as a bag of apples (5 lb), a textbook (3 lb), and a bag of sugar or flour (1 lb or 5 lb). Write each weight for students to see. Have students lift each of the items and match them with the written weights.

After

7. Discuss the solution.
8. Discuss how to check if the solution is reasonable.
9. Give the problem an extension as needed.

Check the Answer

What operation can you use to check your answer? Explain. (Sample answer: Addition; I can use repeated addition to find $0.38 + 0.38 + 0.38 + 0.38 + 0.38 = 1.9$.)

Ask: Is it reasonable that the bag of apples weighs less on Mars than it does on Earth? Why? (Sample answer: Yes, it is reasonable that the bag of apples weighs less on Mars because an object's weight on Mars relative to an object's weight on Earth is less than 1.)

Extension

Ask: What would a 1 pound bag of apples weigh on Mars? Why? (0.38 pounds; Sample answer: An object's weight on Mars relative to an object's weight on Earth is 0.38. I know $1 \times 0.38 = 0.38$.)

Today's Challenge Teacher's Guide

Allie weighs 82 pounds on Earth. How much would she weigh on Venus? Write and solve an equation.

Planet	Weight Relative to Earth
Mercury	0.38
Venus	0.90
Earth	1.00
Mars	0.38
Jupiter	2.36
Saturn	0.92
Uranus	0.89
Neptune	1.13

TEACHING ACTIONS	GUIDING QUESTIONS	DIFFERENTIATED INSTRUCTION

Before

1. Read the problem.
2. Ask guiding questions.
3. Discuss possible solution strategies.

Make Sense of the Problem

Help students understand the problem:

- How much does Allie weigh on Earth? (82 pounds)
- What are you asked to find? (How much Allie would weigh on Venus)
- What are you asked to do to find the answer? (Write and solve an equation.)

During

4. Observe students.
5. Ask guiding questions as needed.
6. Have students check if their solutions are reasonable.

Persevere in Solving the Problem

If students need help, ask:

- Which operation will you use in your equation? (Multiplication)
- Which number from the table will you use to multiply by Allie's weight? Why? (0.90; That is the weight of an object on Venus relative to the same object on Earth.)
- What equation can you write? (Sample answer: $82 \times 0.90 = w$)

SOLUTION Allie would weigh 73.8 pounds on Venus; Sample answer: $82 \times 0.90 = w$; $w = 73.8$ pounds

Extra Support

If students struggle with the idea of weight relative to Earth, remind them that the numbers in the table are for comparisons of weights of objects on the various planets. Say: Suppose an object on Earth weighs 1 pound. What would it weigh on Saturn? (0.92 pounds) Keep giving examples until students understand the concept.

After

7. Discuss the solution.
8. Discuss how to check if the solution is reasonable.
9. Give the problem an extension as needed.

Check the Answer

Ask: Could you use repeated addition to solve the problem? Explain. (Sample answer: Yes, but adding 0.9 eighty-two times is not a good way to solve the problem because it would take too long and it would be easy to make a mistake.)

Ask: How can you use estimation to check that your answer is reasonable? (Sample answer: I can round 0.90 to 1. Then I can find 82×1, which gives an estimate of 82 pounds. So, 73.8 pounds is reasonable.)

Extension

Allie's twin brother Alex weighs 92 pounds on Earth. How much would he weigh on Venus? Write and solve an equation. (Alex would weigh 82.8 pounds on Venus; Sample answer: $92 \times 0.90 = w$; $w = 82.8$ pounds.)

A spaceship has room for three passengers. However, the combined weight of the passengers on Uranus must be between 200 and 225 pounds. Give three possible Earth weights, each less than 100 pounds, for the three passengers. Explain how you know these weights work.

Planet	Weight Relative to Earth
Mercury	0.38
Venus	0.90
Earth	1.00
Mars	0.38
Jupiter	2.36
Saturn	0.92
Uranus	0.89
Neptune	1.13

TEACHING ACTIONS	GUIDING QUESTIONS	DIFFERENTIATED INSTRUCTION
Before 1. Read the problem. 2. Ask guiding questions. 3. Discuss possible solution strategies.	**Make Sense of the Problem** Help students understand the problem: • What must be the combined weight of the passengers on Uranus? (Between 200 and 225 pounds) • What are you asked to find? (Three possible Earth weights for the passengers)	**Vocabulary Review** Review the meaning of the term *mass*. Discuss the difference between *weight* and *mass*, which does not change for the different planets.
During 4. Observe students. 5. Ask guiding questions as needed. 6. Have students check if their solutions are reasonable.	**Persevere in Solving the Problem** If students need help, ask: • If you know an Earth weight, how do you find the weight on Uranus? (Multiply by 0.89) • What do you know about each Earth weight? (Each must be less than 100 pounds) • What is one way you could find three possible weights? (Sample answer: Estimate using three Earth weights that are less than but close to 100. See if the sum on Uranus is between 200 and 225.) **SOLUTION** Sample answer: 70, 80, and 90 pounds; 70 + 80 + 90 = 240; 0.89 × 240 = 213.6. The sum of 213.6 pounds on Uranus is between 200 and 225 pounds.	**Extra Support** If students are having difficulty finding the solution, have them work in small groups. Have each group try to find three weights that work. Then discuss as a class how students found their answers.
After 7. Discuss the solution. 8. Discuss how to check if the solution is reasonable. 9. Give the problem an extension as needed.	**Check the Answer** Ask: Should the combined weights on Earth be greater than or less than the combined weights on Uranus? (Greater than) To check if their solutions are reasonable, ask students to double-check that the combined Earth weights are 225 pounds or greater. The weight relative to Earth for Uranus is 0.89, so the weights on Earth and Uranus will be close.	**Extension** Say: Sharon weighs 96 pounds on Neptune. About how much would she weigh on Venus? (About 76 pounds; 96 ÷ 1.13 = 84.9; 84.9 × 0.90 = 76.4)

Today's Challenge Teacher's Guide

Max weighs 93 pounds on Earth. How much more would he weigh on Saturn than on Mercury? Explain how to find the answer.

Planet	Weight Relative to Earth
Mercury	0.38
Venus	0.90
Earth	1.00
Mars	0.38
Jupiter	2.36
Saturn	0.92
Uranus	0.89
Neptune	1.13

TEACHING ACTIONS	GUIDING QUESTIONS	DIFFERENTIATED INSTRUCTION
Before 1. Read the problem. 2. Ask guiding questions. 3. Discuss possible solution strategies.	**Make Sense of the Problem** Help students understand the problem: • How much does Max weigh on Earth? (93 pounds) • What are you asked to find? (How much more Max would weigh on Saturn than he would on Mercury) • What else are you asked to explain? (How I found my answer)	
During 4. Observe students. 5. Ask guiding questions as needed. 6. Have students check if their solutions are reasonable.	**Persevere in Solving the Problem** If students need help, ask: • What is the first step to find the answer? (Find how much Max would weigh on Saturn and how much he would weigh on Mercury.) • What words tell you which operation to use next? Which operation will you use? (*How much more*; subtraction) **SOLUTION** Max would weigh 50.22 more pounds on Saturn. $0.92 \times 93 = 85.56$ pounds on Saturn; $0.38 \times 93 = 35.34$ pounds on Mercury; $85.56 - 35.34 = 50.22$	**Extra Support** If students have trouble finding the solution, encourage them to draw a picture. Have students draw three planets with a boy standing on each. Have students write the weight relative to the Earth value from the table for each planet.
After 7. Discuss the solution. 8. Discuss how to check if the solution is reasonable. 9. Give the problem an extension as needed.	**Check the Answer** Ask: Why is it important to find Max's weight on both Saturn and Mercury? (Sample answer: You need to find the difference between those weights.) Discuss whether students answered the right question. If the answer given is 85.56 or 35.34, students found Max's weight on Saturn or Mercury, respectively, instead of finding how much *more* he would weigh on Saturn than he would on Mercury.	**Extension** Say: Mr. Gerard weighs 195 pounds on Earth. How much more would he weigh on Uranus than on Mars? (99.45 pounds; $195 \times 0.89 = 173.55$; $195 \times 0.38 = 74.1$; $173.55 - 74.1 = 99.45$

Today's Challenge Teacher's Guide

About how many pounds of nuts did each walnut tree produce this year, on average? Show how to find an estimate.

Type of Tree	Number of Producing Trees on Jim's Family Farm	Pounds of Nuts Produced This Year
Pecan	14	1,372
Walnut	21	1,680
Almond	29	435

TEACHING ACTIONS	GUIDING QUESTIONS	DIFFERENTIATED INSTRUCTION
Before 1. Read the problem. 2. Ask guiding questions. 3. Discuss possible solution strategies.	**Make Sense of the Problem** Help students understand the problem: • What are you asked to find? (About how many pounds of nuts each walnut tree produced this year, on average) • What else are you asked to do? (Show how to find an estimate)	**Vocabulary Review** Review the meaning of the term *data*. Explain that data are often listed in a table to make the information easy to read and analyze.
During 4. Observe students. 5. Ask guiding questions as needed. 6. Have students check if their solutions are reasonable.	**Persevere in Solving the Problem** If students need help, ask: • How many total pounds of nuts did the walnut trees produce this year? (1,680 pounds) How many walnut trees are there? (21) • How can you find the number of pounds one tree produced? (Sample answer: Divide 1,680 by 21.) • What strategies can you use to estimate quotients? (Sample answer: Rounding or compatible numbers) What compatible numbers can you use to estimate how many pounds of nuts each walnut tree produced this year? (Sample answer: 1,600 and 20) **SOLUTION** Each walnut tree produced about 80 pounds of nuts this year. I used compatible numbers to estimate 1,680 ÷ 21. The numbers 1,600 and 20 are close to 1,680 and 21. I found 1,600 ÷ 20 = 80.	**ELL Support** Make sure all students know that pecans, walnuts, and almonds are types of nuts and that they grow on trees. Then, to help them solve the problem, talk about the important and unimportant information given in the chart. Point out that for this problem, students will need to look only at the row for *walnut* trees.
After 7. Discuss the solution. 8. Discuss how to check if the solution is reasonable. 9. Give the problem an extension as needed.	**Check the Answer** Ask: How did you know whether to multiply or divide to find the estimate? (Sample answer: I knew the total number of pounds of nuts produced by the walnut trees, and I wanted to find about how many pounds were produced per tree.) To check if their solutions are reasonable, ask students to multiply the estimate they found by the divisor they used. The product they get should be the dividend they used for the estimate.	**Extension** Say: Last year, there were two fewer walnut trees and 250 fewer pounds of nuts produced. About how many pounds of nuts did each walnut tree produce on average last year? (Sample answer: About 70 pounds; 21 − 2 = 19 trees; 1,680 − 250 = 1,430 pounds; I used compatible numbers to find 1,400 ÷ 20 = 70.)

Today's Challenge Teacher's Guide

Jim is in 5th grade. About how many pounds of walnuts has the farm produced in his lifetime? Choose an age for Jim. Explain your reasoning.

Type of Tree	Number of Producing Trees on Jim's Family Farm	Pounds of Nuts Produced This Year
Pecan	14	1,372
Walnut	21	1,680
Almond	29	435

TEACHING ACTIONS	GUIDING QUESTIONS	DIFFERENTIATED INSTRUCTION

Before

1. Read the problem.
2. Ask guiding questions.
3. Discuss possible solution strategies.

Make Sense of the Problem

Help students understand the problem:

- What do you know about Jim? (He is in 5th grade.)
- What do you need to find? (About how many pounds of walnuts the farm has produced in his lifetime)
- What do you need to choose? (An age for Jim)

During

4. Observe students.
5. Ask guiding questions as needed.
6. Have students check if their solutions are reasonable.

Persevere in Solving the Problem

If students need help, ask:

- Which operation will you use? (Multiplication) Why? (Sample answer: You need to multiply the number of years by the number of pounds of walnuts produced each year.)
- How can you estimate to find the answer? (Sample answer: Round each number, and then multiply.)
- What is 1,680 rounded to the nearest hundred? (1,700) If Jim is in 5th grade, how old could he be? (11 years old)

> **SOLUTION** Sample answer: The farm has produced about 17,000 pounds of walnuts in Jim's lifetime. Jim could be 11 years old; I used rounding to estimate. 11 × 1,680 is about 10 × 1,700 = 17,000.

Extra Support

Help struggling students think about the problem in smaller parts by asking them questions. Ask: How old could Jim be? (Sample answer: 11) What information do you need from the table? (1,680 pounds of walnuts were produced this year.) How will you use both pieces of information to find an estimate? (Sample answer: I can round 1,680 to 1,700 and 11 to 10. Then I can find 1,700 × 10.)

After

7. Discuss the solution.
8. Discuss how to check if the solution is reasonable.
9. Give the problem an extension as needed.

Check the Answer

Ask: Why do you need to choose an age for Jim? (Sample answer: I need to know what number to multiply by 1,700.)

To check if their solutions are reasonable, have students share their answers with the class. Ask the students with the least and greatest answers to explain how they found their answers. Discuss whether their estimates are reasonable.

Extension

Ask: About how many pounds of pecans, walnuts, and almonds has the farm produced during Jim's dad's lifetime? Choose an age for Jim's dad. (Sample answer: 38 years old; about 140,000 pounds; 1,372 + 1,680 + 435 = 3,487; 3,500 × 40 = 140,000)

Jim's family spent $1,498 this year on the pecan trees, including the cost to harvest the nuts. They sold the pecans for $4,488. How much profit did they make on each pecan tree? Write equations to show how to estimate the solution. Profit is income minus cost.

Type of Tree	Number of Producing Trees on Jim's Family Farm	Pounds of Nuts Produced This Year
Pecan	14	1,372
Walnut	21	1,680
Almond	29	435

TEACHING ACTIONS	GUIDING QUESTIONS	DIFFERENTIATED INSTRUCTION

Before

1. Read the problem.
2. Ask guiding questions.
3. Discuss possible solution strategies.

Make Sense of the Problem

Help students understand the problem:

- How much did Jim's family spend on pecan trees this year? ($1,498)
- What are you asked to find? (How much profit the farm made on each pecan tree)

Vocabulary Review

Review the terms *profit*, *income*, and *cost*. Re-read the last sentence in the problem and give examples.

During

4. Observe students.
5. Ask guiding questions as needed.
6. Have students check if their solutions are reasonable.

Persevere in Solving the Problem

If students need help, ask:

- What did Jim's family spend this year on the pecan trees? ($1,498) How much did they sell the pecans for? ($4,488)
- What equation can you write to find the profit from all of the pecan trees? ($p = 4,488 - 1,498$)
- How can you find the profit from one pecan tree? (Divide the profit from all of the pecan trees by the number of pecan trees)

SOLUTION Sample answer: The profit from each tree is about $200. Profit is income minus cost; $p = 4,488 - 1,498$, so $p = 2,990$; I used compatible numbers to estimate the profit they make on each tree or $2,990 \div 14$. The numbers 3,000 and 15 are close to 2,990 and 14; $3,000 \div 15 = n$, so $n = 200$.

ELL Support

Read the problem with students, making a list of the more difficult words, such as *harvest*, *profit*, and *income*. Say the words, have students repeat them, and explain their meaning as used in the problem. For practice, use sentence frames such as the following: When the nuts are ready to be picked, we _____ them. (harvest)

After

7. Discuss the solution.
8. Discuss how to check if the solution is reasonable.
9. Give the problem an extension as needed.

Check the Answer

Ask: How do you know to find an estimate rather than an exact answer? (Sample answer: I am asked to write equations to show how to *estimate* the solution.)

Discuss if students' solutions are reasonable. If $300 is given as the estimate, students most likely rounded 14 to 10. Discuss with students that a better estimate would be $3,000 \div 15 = $200, because it is closer to the exact answer.

Extension

Say: Suppose next year Jim's family farm reduces its costs and sells the pecans for $5,488. If the profit on each pecan tree is $310, what is an estimate for the costs? (Sample answer: $300 \times 15 = $4,500, the estimated profit on all of the pecan trees; $5,500 - $4,500 = $1,000, the estimate for the costs)

Today's Challenge Teacher's Guide

This year Jim's family gets $4 per pound of pecans, $3 per pound of walnuts, and $2 per pound of almonds. All the money from the nuts will go into Jim's college savings account. How much money should go into the account in all? Explain your reasoning.

Type of Tree	Number of Producing Trees on Jim's Family Farm	Pounds of Nuts Produced This Year
Pecan	14	1,372
Walnut	21	1,680
Almond	29	435

TEACHING ACTIONS	GUIDING QUESTIONS	DIFFERENTIATED INSTRUCTION

Before

1. Read the problem.
2. Ask guiding questions.
3. Discuss possible solution strategies.

Make Sense of the Problem

Help students understand the problem:

- Where can you find how many pounds of each kind of nut were produced this year? (In the table)
- What are you asked to find? (The amount of money in all that will go into the account)

During

4. Observe students.
5. Ask guiding questions as needed.
6. Have students check if their solutions are reasonable.

Persevere in Solving the Problem

If students need help, ask:

- How can you find the amount of money received for the nuts from one type of tree? (Multiply the price per pound by the number of pounds.)
- What equation can you write to find the amount received for almonds this year? ($a = 435 \times 2$) From pecans? ($p = 1,372 \times 4$) From walnuts? ($w = 1,680 \times 3$)
- What is the next step after you find the total received for each type of nut? (Add the three amounts to find the funds for all of the nuts this year.)

> **SOLUTION** $11,398; Sample answer: For each type of nut, multiply the number of pounds by the amount per pound the family gets. Then add the products. $435 \times \$2 = \$870$; $1,372 \times \$4 = \$5,488$; $1,680 \times \$3 = \$5,040$; $\$870 + \$5,488 + \$5,040 = \$11,398$

Extra Support

If students have trouble finding the solution, encourage them to make a separate table. Have them label the rows *Pecan,* *Walnut,* and *Almond,* and label the columns with the dollar amount per pound per nut, the pounds of nuts produced per year, and the total amount for each type of nut.

After

7. Discuss the solution.
8. Discuss how to check if the solution is reasonable.
9. Give the problem an extension as needed.

Check the Answer

Ask: How can you check that each equation is correct? (Sample answer: I can use division to check each equation. For example, $\$870 \div 2 = \$425$. Because $425 is a factor in one of the original equations I wrote, I know my answer is correct.)

Use estimation to check if the solution is reasonable. (Sample answer: I rounded each product to the nearest hundred: $870 to $900, $5,488 to $5,500, and $5,040 to $5,000, and then add the three rounded numbers. The estimate is $11,400, which is close to the exact answer.)

Extension

Say: Suppose Jim's family decides to keep $3 per tree to care for the trees. How much would the family deposit into Jim's college savings account then? Explain. ($11,206; $14 + 21 + 29 = 64$ trees; $64 \times \$3$ per tree = $192; $\$11,398 - \$192 = \$11,206$)

5 more trees should start producing almonds next year. How many total pounds of almonds should the farm produce next year? Write equations to show how to find the solution.

Type of Tree	Number of Producing Trees on Jim's Family Farm	Pounds of Nuts Produced This Year
Pecan	14	1,372
Walnut	21	1,680
Almond	29	435

TEACHING ACTIONS	GUIDING QUESTIONS	DIFFERENTIATED INSTRUCTION
Before 1. Read the problem. 2. Ask guiding questions. 3. Discuss possible solution strategies.	**Make Sense of the Problem** Help students understand the problem: • How many more almond trees should start producing next year? (Five) • What are you asked to find? (How many pounds of almonds should be produced next year) • What else are you asked to do? (Write equations to show how to find the answer)	
During 4. Observe students. 5. Ask guiding questions as needed. 6. Have students check if their solutions are reasonable.	**Persevere in Solving the Problem** If students need help, ask: • What do you need to find first? (The number of pounds of almonds produced by one tree) • How many pounds of almonds are produced by 29 trees? (435 pounds) • What equation can you write to find the number of pounds of almonds produced by one tree? (Sample answer: $435 \div 29 = n$)	**ELL Support** To make sure students understand the question, encourage them to rephrase the parts of the problem. For example, to start, say: The farm will have five more almond trees next year.

SOLUTION The farm should produce 510 pounds of almonds next year. 29 trees produce 435 pounds of almonds; $n = 435 \div 29$, so $n = 15$; $m = 5 \times 15$, so $m = 75$; $p = 435 + 75$, so $p = 510$.

| **After** 7. Discuss the solution. 8. Discuss how to check if the solution is reasonable. 9. Give the problem an extension as needed. | **Check the Answer** Ask: Why is it important to find the number of pounds produced by one tree? (Sample answer: I need to find the number of pounds produced by 1 tree so that I can find the number of pounds produced by 5 trees.) To check if their solutions are reasonable, ask students to subtract 435 from their answer and then divide by 5. They should arrive at 15, the number of pounds produced by one tree. | **Extension** Say: Several more pecan trees will start producing nuts next year. 1,960 pounds of pecans will be produced in all. How many new trees will begin producing nuts? (6; 1,372 lb ÷ 14 trees = 98 lb per tree; 1,960 lb − 1,372 lb = 588 more lb; 588 lb ÷ 98 lb = 6 new trees) |

How much more of the atmosphere is nitrogen than all other gases combined? Explain how to find the answer.

Gas	Part of Atmosphere
Nitrogen	0.79
Oxygen	0.20
Other gases	0.01

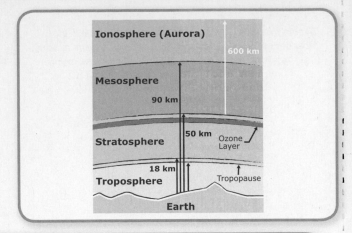

TEACHING ACTIONS	GUIDING QUESTIONS	DIFFERENTIATED INSTRUCTION
Before 1. Read the problem. 2. Ask guiding questions. 3. Discuss possible solution strategies.	**Make Sense of the Problem** Help students understand the problem: • What are you asked to find? (How much more of the atmosphere is nitrogen than all other gases combined) • Where will you find the information to solve this problem? (In the table)	
During 4. Observe students. 5. Ask guiding questions as needed. 6. Have students check if their solutions are reasonable.	**Persevere in Solving the Problem** If students need help, ask: • What part of the atmosphere is nitrogen? (0.79) • How can you find the part of the atmosphere that is made up of all other gases combined? (Add 0.20 and 0.01) • What words tell you to subtract to find the answer? (How much more) **SOLUTION** Nitrogen makes up 0.58 more than all other gases combined. Nitrogen is 0.79 of the atmosphere; Oxygen and other gases make up $0.20 + 0.01 = 0.21$; $0.79 - 0.21 = 0.58$.	**ELL Support** Make sure students understand that they will need to both add and subtract as they solve this problem. Point out clue words in the problem such as *how much more* and *all*. Explain that these words help students understand the processes they will need to use to solve the problem.
After 7. Discuss the solution. 8. Discuss how to check if the solution is reasonable. 9. Give the problem an extension as needed.	**Check the Answer** Ask: Should the answer be greater than or less than 1? How do you know? (Less than 1; Sample answer: The answer will be just part of the atmosphere, so it must be a number less than 1.) To check if their solutions are reasonable, ask students to add their answer to the parts of the atmosphere that are oxygen and other gases. The sum should be 0.79.	**Extension** Ask: Does nitrogen make up more or less than half of the gases in the atmosphere? Explain. (Nitrogen makes up more than half; Sample answer: One half is equal to 0.5 and $0.79 > 0.5$.)

Today's Challenge Teacher's Guide

If the nitrogen in the troposphere was separated out from the other gases, how many kilometers thick would the nitrogen in the troposphere be? Explain how to find the answer.

Gas	Part of Atmosphere
Nitrogen	0.79
Oxygen	0.20
Other gases	0.01

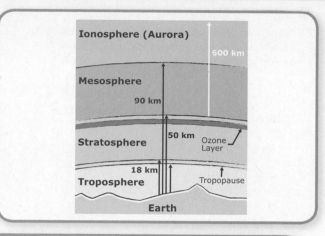

Ionosphere (Aurora)
600 km
Mesosphere
90 km
Stratosphere — 50 km — Ozone Layer
18 km
Troposphere — Tropopause
Earth

TEACHING ACTIONS	GUIDING QUESTIONS	DIFFERENTIATED INSTRUCTION

Before

1. Read the problem.
2. Ask guiding questions.
3. Discuss possible solution strategies.

Make Sense of the Problem

Help students understand the problem:

- Which layer of the atmosphere is this problem about? (The troposphere)
- Where can you find the thickness of the troposphere? (In the diagram)

Vocabulary Review

Review the term *kilometer* and its abbreviation *km*. Remind students that 1 kilometer is equal to 1,000 meters.

During

4. Observe students.
5. Ask guiding questions as needed.
6. Have students check if their solutions are reasonable.

Persevere in Solving the Problem

If students need help, ask:

- How thick is the troposphere? (18 km)
- Which operation do you use to find how many kilometers thick the nitrogen would be in the troposphere? (Multiplication)
- What equation can you write to model the problem? (18 km × 0.79 = 14.22 km)

SOLUTION The nitrogen in the troposphere would be 14.22 km thick. The troposphere is 18 km thick. Nitrogen is 0.79 of the atmosphere. To solve, I can multiply the thickness of the troposphere by the part of the atmosphere that is nitrogen: 18 × 0.79 = 14.22.

Extra Support

If students have trouble finding the solution, suggest that they draw a picture. Have them draw the troposphere and then use shading to show about 0.79 (about $\frac{3}{4}$). Guide students to see that they need to find part of 18 km.

After

7. Discuss the solution.
8. Discuss how to check if the solution is reasonable.
9. Give the problem an extension as needed.

Check the Answer

Ask: Why do you need both the table and the diagram? (Sample answer: Both have information you need to solve the problem.)

To check if their solutions are reasonable, ask students if their answer is between 9 and 18. The part of atmosphere for nitrogen is 0.79, so the answer should be greater than half of 18 and less than 18.

Extension

Say: If the oxygen in the tropopause and stratosphere was separated from the other gases, how many kilometers thick would the oxygen be? Explain. (10 km; 50 km × 0.2 = 10 km)

Today's Challenge Teacher's Guide

Which layer or combination of layers is about 2.5 times as thick as another layer or combination of layers? Explain your answer.

Gas	Part of Atmosphere
Nitrogen	0.79
Oxygen	0.20
Other gases	0.01

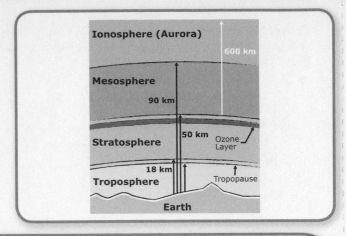

TEACHING ACTIONS	GUIDING QUESTIONS	DIFFERENTIATED INSTRUCTION
Before 1. Read the problem. 2. Ask guiding questions. 3. Discuss possible solution strategies.	**Make Sense of the Problem** Help students understand the problem: • What are you asked to find? (The layer or combination of layers that is about 2.5 times as thick as another layer or combination of layers) • Will you use the diagram or table to answer the question? (The diagram)	
During 4. Observe students. 5. Ask guiding questions as needed. 6. Have students check if their solutions are reasonable.	**Persevere in Solving the Problem** If students need help, ask: • What do you need to find in the diagram? (One or more layers that are between 2 and 3 times as thick as another layer or layers) • What is one way you can find the answer? (Sample answer: Use number sense to choose layers and then find if one layer, or a combination of layers, is about 2.5 times as thick as the other.) **SOLUTION** Sample answer: The mesosphere is about 2.5 times as thick as the troposphere. The mesosphere is $90 - 50 = 40$ km thick. The troposphere is 18 km thick. $18 \times 2.5 = 45$, which is close to 40.	**ELL Support** For students who need extra language support, read the word problem together. Encourage them to rephrase the problem. For example, instead of saying *layer or combination of layers*, have them say *one or more layers*.
After 7. Discuss the solution. 8. Discuss how to check if the solution is reasonable. 9. Give the problem an extension as needed.	**Check the Answer** Ask: What is another way to say *about 2.5 times as thick*? (Sample answer: *Between 2 and 3 times as thick*) Discuss with students how to check their answer when there may be more than one correct answer. Regardless of the layers they chose, students should find that one thickness is about 2.5 times as thick as the other.	**Extension** Say: The tropopause is 4 km thick. Which layer is exactly 10 times as thick as the tropopause? How thick is that layer? (The mesosphere is 10 times as thick as the tropopause; mesosphere: 40 km)

Today's Challenge Teacher's Guide

The ionosphere is how many times as thick as the mesosphere? Explain how to find the answer.

Gas	Part of Atmosphere
Nitrogen	0.79
Oxygen	0.20
Other gases	0.01

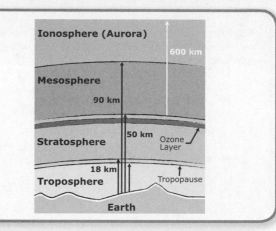

TEACHING ACTIONS	GUIDING QUESTIONS	DIFFERENTIATED INSTRUCTION

Before

1. Read the problem.
2. Ask guiding questions.
3. Discuss possible solution strategies.

Make Sense of the Problem

Help students understand the problem:

- What are you asked to find? (How many times as thick as the mesosphere is the ionosphere)
- Where will you find the information to solve this problem? (In the diagram)

During

4. Observe students.
5. Ask guiding questions as needed.
6. Have students check if their solutions are reasonable.

Persevere in Solving the Problem

If students need help, ask:

- What equations can you write to find the thicknesses of the mesosphere and the ionosphere in the diagram? (Mesosphere: $90 - 50 = 40$; ionosphere: $600 - 40 = 560$)
- What operation do you use to find how many times thicker one layer is than another layer? (Division)

> **SOLUTION** The ionosphere is 14 times as thick as the mesosphere. Mesosphere: $90 - 50 = 40$ km; ionosphere: $600 - 40 = 560$ km; $560 \div 40 = 14$.

Extra Support

If students have trouble finding the thickness of the ionosphere, tell them that they need to compute the thickness of the mesosphere first and then use that answer to compute the thickness of the ionosphere.

After

7. Discuss the solution.
8. Discuss how to check if the solution is reasonable.
9. Give the problem an extension as needed.

Check the Answer

Ask: Why is it important to find the thickness of each layer first? (Sample answer: You need to find the quotient of those two numbers.)

Discuss whether students answered the right question. Students who got an answer of 15 probably compared the thickness of the ionosphere and the mesosphere combined to the thickness of the mesosphere.

Extension

Say: Explain why the thickness of the mesosphere is not 90 km. (Sample answer: 90 km is the distance the mesosphere is from the Earth's surface rather than the thickness of the mesosphere.)

Today's Challenge Teacher's Guide

How many times as thick as the troposphere is the mesosphere and ionosphere combined? Draw a diagram and write an equation to solve.

Gas	Part of Atmosphere
Nitrogen	0.79
Oxygen	0.20
Other gases	0.01

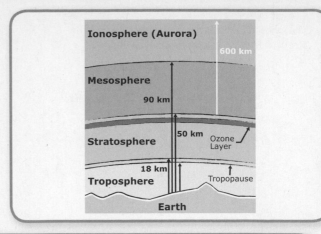

TEACHING ACTIONS	GUIDING QUESTIONS	DIFFERENTIATED INSTRUCTION

Before

1. Read the problem.
2. Ask guiding questions.
3. Discuss possible solution strategies.

Make Sense of the Problem

Help students understand the problem:

- What are you asked to find? (How many times as thick as the troposphere is the mesosphere and ionosphere combined)
- What else are you asked to do? (Draw a diagram and write an equation)

Vocabulary Review

Review the definition of the term *equation*. Point out that *equation* comes from the same Latin root as the word *equal*.

During

4. Observe students.
5. Ask guiding questions as needed.
6. Have students check if their solutions are reasonable.

Persevere in Solving the Problem

If students need help, ask:

- What is the first step? (Sample answer: Find the combined thickness of the mesosphere and ionosphere.)
- Describe in words what the equation will show. (Sample answer: The combined thickness of the two layers divided by the thickness of the troposphere is the number of times as thick.)

ELL Support

Make sure students know how to read equations with variables. Write: $70 \div 10 = n$ and $2 + x = 30$. Then have students listen and repeat as you read: *Seventy divided by ten is what number?* and *Two plus what number is thirty?*

SOLUTION Sample answer: The two layers combined are about 33 times as thick. $600 \div 18 = n$; $n = 33.\overline{3}$. Sample diagram:

600 km

18 km	———————————— →
	?

After

7. Discuss the solution.
8. Discuss how to check if the solution is reasonable.
9. Give the problem an extension as needed.

Check the Answer

Ask: To check the reasonableness of your answer, can you use compatible numbers to estimate the quotient? Why? (Yes; Sample answer: 20 is close to 18. It is easy to find $600 \div 20 = 30$. This estimate is close to my answer, 33.)

To check if their solutions are reasonable, ask students to multiply their answer by the thickness of the troposphere. They should arrive at an amount close to the combined thickness of the mesosphere and ionosphere.

Extension

Ask: About how many times as thick as the troposphere is the stratosphere? Use compatible numbers to find the answer. (Sample answer: About 2 times as thick; $50 - 18 = 32$; $32 \div 18$ is about $36 \div 18 = 2$.)

How many quarter notes have the same length as a dotted half note? Justify your answer.

Musical Notes

Musical Note	Name	Relative Length
o	Whole note	1
♩	Half note	$\frac{1}{2}$
♩	Quarter note	$\frac{1}{4}$
♪	Eighth note	$\frac{1}{8}$
♪	Sixteenth note	$\frac{1}{16}$
♩.	Dotted half note	$\frac{3}{4}$
♩.	Dotted quarter note	$\frac{3}{8}$
♫	Pair of eighth notes	$\frac{2}{8}$

TEACHING ACTIONS	GUIDING QUESTIONS	DIFFERENTIATED INSTRUCTION

Before

1. Read the problem.
2. Ask guiding questions.
3. Discuss possible solution strategies.

Make Sense of the Problem

Help students understand the problem:

- What are you asked to find? (The number of quarter notes that have the same length as a dotted half note)
- What else are you asked to do? (Justify my answer)
- How can you use the table? (Sample answer: The table shows the lengths of musical notes. I can find the length of a quarter note and dotted half note using the table.)

Vocabulary Review

Review the terms *numerator* and *denominator*. Ask students to write a fraction and circle the numerator.

During

4. Observe students.
5. Ask guiding questions as needed.
6. Have students check if their solutions are reasonable.

Persevere in Solving the Problem

If students need help, ask:

- What is the length of a dotted half note? ($\frac{3}{4}$)
- What is the length of a quarter note? ($\frac{1}{4}$)
- How can you find how many quarter notes have a length of $\frac{3}{4}$? (Sample answer: I can keep adding $\frac{1}{4}$s, until I get $\frac{3}{4}$.)

SOLUTION 3 quarter notes; Sample answer: A dotted half note has a length of $\frac{3}{4}$ and a quarter note has a length of $\frac{1}{4}$. Since $\frac{1}{4} + \frac{1}{4} + \frac{1}{4} = \frac{3}{4}$, 3 quarter notes have the same length as a dotted half note.

Extra Support

If students have trouble finding the solution, encourage them to model the problem using fraction strips. Have them try building $\frac{3}{4}$ using $\frac{1}{4}$ strips.

After

7. Discuss the solution.
8. Discuss how to check if the solution is reasonable.
9. Give the problem an extension as needed.

Check the Answer

Ask: When finding the sum of $\frac{1}{4} + \frac{1}{4} + \frac{1}{4}$, does the denominator change? (No) Why not? (Sample answer: The denominator shows the number of equal parts the whole is divided into. The numerator shows how many equal parts there are. Only the numerator changes in the sum of $\frac{1}{4} + \frac{1}{4} + \frac{1}{4}$.)

Discuss whether students added the fractions correctly. If students had difficulty finding the number of quarter notes, have them use a number line divided into fourths. Have them count the number of $\frac{1}{4}$ sections that equal $\frac{3}{4}$.

Extension

Ask: How many eighth notes have the same length as a a dotted quarter note? Justify your answer. (3 eighth notes; An eighth note has a length of $\frac{1}{8}$ and a dotted quarter note has a length of $\frac{3}{8}$. Add $\frac{1}{8} + \frac{1}{8} + \frac{1}{8} = \frac{3}{8}$.)

Today's Challenge Teacher's Guide

What note has the same length as 2 sixteenth notes? Justify your answer.

Musical Notes

Musical Note	Name	Relative Length
o	Whole note	1
♩	Half note	$\frac{1}{2}$
♩	Quarter note	$\frac{1}{4}$
♪	Eighth note	$\frac{1}{8}$
♬	Sixteenth note	$\frac{1}{16}$
♩.	Dotted half note	$\frac{3}{4}$
♩.	Dotted quarter note	$\frac{3}{8}$
♫	Pair of eighth notes	$\frac{2}{8}$

TEACHING ACTIONS	GUIDING QUESTIONS	DIFFERENTIATED INSTRUCTION

Before

1. Read the problem.
2. Ask guiding questions.
3. Discuss possible solution strategies.

Make Sense of the Problem

Help students understand the problem:

- What are you asked to find? (The note that has the same length as 2 sixteenth notes)
- What is the length for one sixteenth note? ($\frac{1}{16}$)
- What else are you asked to do? (Justify my answer)

Review the meaning of the term *equivalent fractions*. Ask students to name two fractions that are equivalent to $\frac{2}{4}$. (Sample answer: $\frac{1}{2}$ and $\frac{4}{8}$)

During

4. Observe students.
5. Ask guiding questions as needed.
6. Have students check if their solutions are reasonable.

Persevere in Solving the Problem

If students need help, ask:

- What fraction do you need to find in the table? (Sample answer: The fraction equivalent to 2 sixteenths)
- How would you write 2 sixteenths as a fraction? ($\frac{2}{16}$)
- What are some ways you can find a fraction equivalent to $\frac{2}{16}$? (Sample answer: Draw a number line, use fraction strips)

SOLUTION Eighth note because $\frac{2}{16}$ is equivalent to $\frac{1}{8}$. Students can justify their answer by drawing a number line or fraction strips.

ELL Support

Make sure all students understand the music terminology in the table. The type of note indicates how long a note is played. For example, a whole note is played the same amount of time as 4 quarter notes.

After

7. Discuss the solution.
8. Discuss how to check if the solution is reasonable.
9. Give the problem an extension as needed.

Check the Answer

Ask: How do you create a fraction that is equivalent to another fraction? (Sample answer: Multiply the numerator and denominator by the same number.)

To check if their solutions are reasonable, ask students to divide both the numerator and denominator of $\frac{2}{16}$ by 2. Students should find that the equivalent fraction is $\frac{1}{8}$.

Extension

Ask: What note has the same length as 8 sixteenth notes? Justify your answer.

(Half note; $\frac{1}{16} + \frac{1}{16} + \frac{1}{16} + \frac{1}{16} + \frac{1}{16} + \frac{1}{16} + \frac{1}{16} + \frac{1}{16} = \frac{8}{16}$; $\frac{8}{16} = \frac{1}{2}$)

Name two different combinations of notes that have the same length as a whole note. Explain your answer.

Musical Notes		
Musical Note	**Name**	**Relative Length**
𝅝	Whole note	1
𝅗𝅥	Half note	$\frac{1}{2}$
♩	Quarter note	$\frac{1}{4}$
♪	Eighth note	$\frac{1}{8}$
𝅘𝅥𝅯	Sixteenth note	$\frac{1}{16}$
𝅗𝅥.	Dotted half note	$\frac{3}{4}$
♩.	Dotted quarter note	$\frac{3}{8}$
♫	Pair of eighth notes	$\frac{2}{8}$

TEACHING ACTIONS	GUIDING QUESTIONS	DIFFERENTIATED INSTRUCTION

Before

1. Read the problem.
2. Ask guiding questions.
3. Discuss possible solution strategies.

Make Sense of the Problem

Help students understand the problem:

- How many combinations of notes will you find? (2 different combinations)
- What should your combinations be equal to? (The length of a whole note)
- What will you explain? (How my combinations are equal in length to 1 whole note)

During

4. Observe students.
5. Ask guiding questions as needed.
6. Have students check if their solutions are reasonable.

Persevere in Solving the Problem

If students need help, ask:

- What is one way you can find an answer to this question? (Sample answer: Begin with a half note, then try to find 2 or more notes that together are equal to another half.)
- Is a half note and three quarter notes a possible answer? Why or why not? (Sample answer: No. 3 quarter notes are equal to $\frac{3}{4}$, which is greater than $\frac{1}{2}$. If I use a half note, the other notes need to equal $\frac{1}{2}$.)

SOLUTION There are many combinations. Sample answer: a half note, two eighth notes, and a quarter note have the same length as a whole note: $\frac{1}{2} + \frac{2}{8} + \frac{1}{4} = \frac{2}{4} + \frac{1}{4} + \frac{1}{4} = \frac{4}{4} = 1$; four quarter notes also have the same length as whole note: $\frac{1}{4} + \frac{1}{4} + \frac{1}{4} + \frac{1}{4} = \frac{4}{4} = 1$.

ELL Support

Discuss the multiple meanings of the word *note*. A note can be a short piece of writing people use to help them remember something. Students may be familiar with taking notes on the reading they do for school. In music, a note refers to the length of a certain sound.

After

7. Discuss the solution.
8. Discuss how to check if the solution is reasonable.
9. Give the problem an extension as needed.

Check the Answer

Ask: Could there be more than one correct answer? Why or why not? (Sample: Yes. There might be more than one combination of fractions that adds up to 1.)

To check if their solutions are reasonable, ask students to change the order of the fractions and add again. Students should find that the sum is still 1.

Extension

Say: Name 3 different ways to make $\frac{3}{8}$ using notes in the table. (Sample answer: a quarter note and an eighth note; three eighth notes; a quarter note and two sixteenth notes)

Today's Challenge Teacher's Guide

Name three notes shorter than a dotted quarter note and three notes longer than a dotted quarter note. Explain your answer.

Musical Notes

Musical Note	Name	Relative Length
o	Whole note	1
♩	Half note	$\frac{1}{2}$
♩	Quarter note	$\frac{1}{4}$
♪	Eighth note	$\frac{1}{8}$
♪	Sixteenth note	$\frac{1}{16}$
♩.	Dotted half note	$\frac{3}{4}$
♩.	Dotted quarter note	$\frac{3}{8}$
♫	Pair of eighth notes	$\frac{2}{8}$

TEACHING ACTIONS	GUIDING QUESTIONS	DIFFERENTIATED INSTRUCTION

Before

1. Read the problem.
2. Ask guiding questions.
3. Discuss possible solution strategies.

Make Sense of the Problem

Help students understand the problem:

- What is the length of a dotted quarter note? ($\frac{3}{8}$)
- How will your answers be related to a dotted quarter note? (3 notes will be shorter than a dotted quarter note and 3 notes will be longer than a dotted quarter note.)

During

4. Observe students.
5. Ask guiding questions as needed.
6. Have students check if their solutions are reasonable.

Persevere in Solving the Problem

If students need help, ask:

- How can you compare fractions? (Sample answer: I can rename fractions so they have the same denominator.)
- How could you explain your answer? (Sample answer: I could use equivalent fractions to show how the length of the notes are shorter or longer than $\frac{3}{8}$.)

SOLUTION Sample answer: Shorter: quarter note, eighth note, and sixteenth note; Longer: half note; dotted half note; whole note. Students may use a number line, fraction strips, or equivalent fractions to explain their answers.

Extra Support

If students have trouble finding the solution, suggest that they draw a model. Have them use a number line to show sixteenths. Then help students find equivalent fractions for eighths, fourths, one half, and a whole. Have students label the number line with the names of the notes.

After

7. Discuss the solution.
8. Discuss how to check if the solution is reasonable.
9. Give the problem an extension as needed.

Check the Answer

Ask: Could there have been different notes longer than the dotted quarter note? Shorter? Why or why not? (Longer: No; There are only 3 notes in the table that are longer than $\frac{3}{8}$. Shorter: Yes; Sample answer: A pair of eighth notes is equal to $\frac{2}{8}$, so they are shorter than $\frac{3}{8}$.)

To make sure their solutions are reasonable, have students choose a different method to compare the fractions. Ask: What other method could you use to compare the fractions? (Students may choose to use a number line, fraction models or strips, or equivalent fractions.)

Extension

Say: Compare each note in the table to a quarter note. Tell whether the note is longer, shorter, or equal to a quarter note. (Longer: whole note, half note, dotted half note, dotted quarter note; Shorter: eighth note, sixteenth note; Equal: pair of eighth notes)

34

How much longer are 1 half note and 1 eighth note together than 1 quarter note? Explain your reasoning.

Musical Notes

Musical Note	Name	Relative Length
𝅝	Whole note	1
𝅗𝅥	Half note	$\frac{1}{2}$
𝅘𝅥	Quarter note	$\frac{1}{4}$
𝅘𝅥𝅮	Eighth note	$\frac{1}{8}$
𝅘𝅥𝅯	Sixteenth note	$\frac{1}{16}$
𝅗𝅥.	Dotted half note	$\frac{3}{4}$
𝅘𝅥.	Dotted quarter note	$\frac{3}{8}$
𝅘𝅥𝅮𝅘𝅥𝅮	Pair of eighth notes	$\frac{2}{8}$

TEACHING ACTIONS	GUIDING QUESTIONS	DIFFERENTIATED INSTRUCTION

Before

1. Read the problem.
2. Ask guiding questions.
3. Discuss possible solution strategies.

Make Sense of the Problem

Help students understand the problem:

- What are you asked to find? (How much longer 1 half note and 1 eighth note are together than 1 quarter note)
- How long is a half note? $(\frac{1}{2})$ An eighth note? $(\frac{1}{8})$ A quarter note? $(\frac{1}{4})$
- What else do you need to do? (Explain your reasoning)

During

4. Observe students.
5. Ask guiding questions as needed.
6. Have students check if their solutions are reasonable.

Persevere in Solving the Problem

If students need help, ask:

- What do you need to do with the lengths for a half note and eighth note? (Add the lengths)
- What do you need to do before you add or subtract fractions? (Make sure the denominators are the same)
- What words tell you to subtract? (How much longer)
- What do you need to subtract? (A quarter note from the sum of the lengths of a half note and an eighth note)

SOLUTION The notes are $\frac{3}{8}$ longer. First, add the half note and eighth note: $\frac{1}{2} + \frac{1}{8} = \frac{4}{8} + \frac{1}{8} = \frac{5}{8}$. Then find how much longer the sum is than a quarter note: $\frac{5}{8} - \frac{1}{4} = \frac{5}{8} - \frac{2}{8} = \frac{3}{8}$.

Extra Support

If students have trouble finding the solution, encourage them to use number lines to find equivalent fractions and to add and subtract fractions.

After

7. Discuss the solution.
8. Discuss how to check if the solution is reasonable.
9. Give the problem an extension as needed.

Check the Answer

Ask: Why is it important to add $\frac{1}{2}$ and $\frac{1}{8}$ first? (Sample answer: You need to find how much longer the combination of the two notes is than a quarter note.)

To check if their solutions are reasonable, ask students to add $\frac{1}{4}$ to their answer. They should find that the sum is $\frac{5}{8}$, the combined value of the half note and eighth note.

Extension

Ask: A dotted half note and a sixteenth note together are $\frac{5}{16}$ longer than which note? (A half note)

Today's Challenge Teacher's Guide

Estimate which activities Brad does for about half of the day. Explain how you know these activities add up to about 12 hours.

Brad's Daily Schedule
Average Time Spent on Activities

Activity	Time in Hours
Eating	$1\frac{3}{5}$
Educational	$7\frac{3}{5}$
Sports and Play	$3\frac{7}{10}$
Sleeping	$8\frac{1}{2}$
Grooming	$\frac{4}{5}$
Other	$1\frac{4}{5}$

TEACHING ACTIONS	GUIDING QUESTIONS	DIFFERENTIATED INSTRUCTION

Before

1. Read the problem.
2. Ask guiding questions.
3. Discuss possible solution strategies.

Make Sense of the Problem

Help students understand the problem:

- What are you asked to find? (Estimate which activities Brad spends about half of the day doing)
- How will you find the answer? (Estimate a sum)
- How many hours in all do the activities need to take? (About 12 hours)

Vocabulary Review

Review the meaning of the term *mixed number*. Ask students to write $\frac{8}{3}$ and $\frac{15}{4}$ as mixed numbers. ($2\frac{2}{3}$; $3\frac{3}{4}$)

During

4. Observe students.
5. Ask guiding questions as needed.
6. Have students check if their solutions are reasonable.

Persevere in Solving the Problem

If students need help, ask:

- How can you estimate when working with mixed numbers? (Round to the nearest whole number)
- What is $3\frac{7}{10}$ rounded to the nearest whole number? (4)
- What are some ways to find the answer? (Sample answer: Make a list or a table with the rounded times; use number sense or reasoning)

SOLUTION Sample answer: $8\frac{1}{2}$ is about 9; $3\frac{7}{10}$ is about 4; $9 + 4 = 13$, and 13 is about 12, so Brad spends about 13 hours or about half the day sleeping and doing sports.

ELL Support

For students who need extra language support, read the problem together. Point out key words such as *estimate* and *half of the day*. Be sure students understand what each of these key words means.

After

7. Discuss the solution.
8. Discuss how to check if the solution is reasonable.
9. Give the problem an extension as needed.

Check the Answer

Ask: Why is it helpful to estimate when solving this problem? (Sample answer: Adding whole numbers is easier than adding mixed numbers.)

Discuss with students how to check their answer when there is more than one possible answer. Since the activities should make up about half the day, the sum of the activity times needs to be about 12.

Extension

Ask: Brad spends about $\frac{1}{8}$ of a day doing which two activities combined? (Grooming and eating; grooming and other)

How many total hours does Brad spend on educational and sports activities each day? Write your answer as a mixed number. Draw a picture and write an equation to show your solution.

Brad's Daily Schedule Average Time Spent on Activities

Activity	Time in Hours
Eating	$1\frac{3}{5}$
Educational	$7\frac{3}{5}$
Sports and Play	$3\frac{7}{10}$
Sleeping	$8\frac{1}{2}$
Grooming	$\frac{4}{5}$
Other	$1\frac{4}{5}$

TEACHING ACTIONS	GUIDING QUESTIONS	DIFFERENTIATED INSTRUCTION

Before

1. Read the problem.
2. Ask guiding questions.
3. Discuss possible solution strategies.

Make Sense of the Problem

Help students understand the problem:

- What are you asked to find? (The time Brad spends on educational and sports activities)
- How should you write your answer? (As a mixed number)
- What else are you asked to do? (Draw a picture and write an equation)

Vocabulary Review

Review the meaning of the term *variable*. Discuss how students can use variables when they write equations to help solve problems.

During

4. Observe students.
5. Ask guiding questions as needed.
6. Have students check if their solutions are reasonable.

Persevere in Solving the Problem

If students need help, ask:

- What equation can you write to find the sum? (Sample answer: $7\frac{3}{5} + 3\frac{7}{10} = n$)
- What common denominator will you use to add the fractions? (Sample answer: 10) What is $\frac{3}{5} + \frac{7}{10}$? Explain. ($\frac{13}{10}$; $\frac{3}{5} = \frac{6}{10}$, and $\frac{6}{10} + \frac{7}{10} = \frac{13}{10}$, which is the same as 1 and $\frac{3}{10}$.)
- What can you draw to help find the answer? (Sample answer: A bar diagram showing that the sum of the two fractions is equal to n)

SOLUTION Brad spends $11\frac{3}{10}$ hours on these activities; $7\frac{3}{5} + 3\frac{7}{10} = n$; $11\frac{3}{10} = n$. Sample drawing:

n	
$7\frac{3}{5}$	$3\frac{7}{10}$

Extra Support

If students have trouble finding the solution, have them work in small groups. Ask students to share methods for adding mixed numbers. Discuss whether students prefer to rename mixed numbers as improper fractions in order to add.

After

7. Discuss the solution.
8. Discuss how to check if the solution is reasonable.
9. Give the problem an extension as needed.

Check the Answer

Ask: How can you estimate to check your answer? (Sample answer: Round each mixed number to the nearest whole number and then add the rounded numbers. $7\frac{3}{5} + 3\frac{7}{10}$ is about $8 + 4$, which equals 12. The answer should be about 12.)

To check if their solutions are reasonable, ask students to subtract $7\frac{3}{5}$ or $3\frac{7}{10}$ from their answer. Students should find that the difference is the other mixed number.

Extension

Ask: Which three activities does Brad spend exactly 10 hours a day doing? (Eating, educational activities, and grooming)

Today's Challenge Teacher's Guide

How many more hours does Brad spend on eating and educational activities combined than he spends on sleeping? Explain your reasoning.

Brad's Daily Schedule Average Time Spent on Activities

Activity	Time in Hours
Eating	$1\frac{3}{5}$
Educational	$7\frac{3}{5}$
Sports and Play	$3\frac{7}{10}$
Sleeping	$8\frac{1}{2}$
Grooming	$\frac{4}{5}$
Other	$1\frac{4}{5}$

TEACHING ACTIONS	GUIDING QUESTIONS	DIFFERENTIATED INSTRUCTION

Before

1. Read the problem.
2. Ask guiding questions.
3. Discuss possible solution strategies.

Make Sense of the Problem

Help students understand the problem:

- What are you asked to find? (How many more hours Brad spends on eating and educational activities combined than he spends on sleeping)
- How much time does he spend sleeping each day? ($8\frac{1}{2}$ hours)

Vocabulary Review

Review the term *common denominator*. Remind students that they need to find a common denominator to add or subtract fractions.

During

4. Observe students.
5. Ask guiding questions as needed.
6. Have students check if their solutions are reasonable.

Persevere in Solving the Problem

If students need help, ask:

- What is the first step? (Find the number of hours Brad spends on eating and educational activities combined)
- What words tell you that you could subtract to solve this problem? (How many more)
- What is a common denominator for $\frac{6}{5}$ and $\frac{1}{2}$? (10)

SOLUTION Brad spends $\frac{7}{10}$ of an hour longer on the two activities than on sleeping; Sample answer: $1\frac{3}{5} + 7\frac{3}{5} = 8\frac{6}{5}$; $8\frac{6}{5} - 8\frac{1}{2} = 8\frac{12}{10} - 8\frac{5}{10} = \frac{7}{10}$.

ELL Support

Point out the word *combined* from the problem. Say: This word tells you to "add together" the number of hours Brad spent on eating and educational activities.

After

7. Discuss the solution.
8. Discuss how to check if the solution is reasonable.
9. Give the problem an extension as needed.

Check the Answer

Ask: Why is it important to add the times for eating and educational activities first? (Sample answer: I need to find how much more time Brad spends doing those activities combined than he does sleeping.)

Discuss whether students answered the right question. If students answered $9\frac{1}{5}$, they found the number of hours Brad spends on eating and educational activities combined, but they did not compare that number to the number of hours Brad spends sleeping.

Extension

Ask: How much more time does Brad spend sleeping in one day than he does eating in four days? Write your answer as a mixed number. ($2\frac{1}{10}$ hours)

Today's Challenge Teacher's Guide

Karla and Brad both spend the same amount of time on grooming and sleeping combined. If Karla only sleeps for $8\frac{1}{5}$ hours, how many hours does she spend on grooming? Explain your reasoning.

Brad's Daily Schedule
Average Time Spent on Activities

Activity	Time in Hours
Eating	$1\frac{3}{5}$
Educational	$7\frac{3}{5}$
Sports and Play	$3\frac{7}{10}$
Sleeping	$8\frac{1}{2}$
Grooming	$\frac{4}{5}$
Other	$1\frac{4}{5}$

TEACHING ACTIONS	GUIDING QUESTIONS	DIFFERENTIATED INSTRUCTION

Before

1. Read the problem.
2. Ask guiding questions.
3. Discuss possible solution strategies.

Make Sense of the Problem

Help students understand the problem:

- What do you know? (Karla and Brad spend the same amount of time on grooming and sleeping combined; Karla sleeps $8\frac{1}{5}$ hours a day)
- What are you asked to find? (How many hours Karla spends on grooming)

During

4. Observe students.
5. Ask guiding questions as needed.
6. Have students check if their solutions are reasonable.

Persevere in Solving the Problem

If students need help, ask:

- How can you find the number of hours each of them spends on grooming and sleeping combined? (Add $\frac{4}{5}$ and $8\frac{1}{2}$)
- If you know the total and you know one part, which operation can you use to find the other part? (Sample answer: Subtraction)

SOLUTION Karla spends $1\frac{1}{10}$ hours on grooming. Sample answer: $8\frac{1}{2} + \frac{4}{5} = 8\frac{5}{10} + \frac{8}{10} = 8\frac{13}{10}$; $8\frac{13}{10} - 8\frac{1}{5} = 8\frac{13}{10} - 8\frac{2}{10} = \frac{11}{10} = 1\frac{1}{10}$ hours

Extra Support

If students have trouble finding the solution, encourage them to approach the problem in a different way. Karla spends less time sleeping. The time that she gains by sleeping less can be added to the grooming time.

After

7. Discuss the solution.
8. Discuss how to check if the solution is reasonable.
9. Give the problem an extension as needed.

Check the Answer

Ask: Should the answer be greater than or less than $\frac{4}{5}$? How do you know? (Greater than $\frac{4}{5}$; Sample answer: Karla spends less time sleeping than Brad, so she must spend more time grooming.)

To check if their solutions are reasonable, ask students to add their answer to $8\frac{1}{5}$. They should find that the sum is the total number of hours Brad spends on both activities, $9\frac{3}{10}$.

Extension

Say: Brad and Jen spend the same amount of time on educational and sports activities combined. What are two possibilities for the hours Jen spends on each activity? Explain. (Sample answer: Brad spends $11\frac{3}{10}$ h on both activities; $8\frac{1}{5}$ h and $3\frac{1}{10}$ h; $6\frac{9}{10}$ h and $4\frac{2}{5}$ h)

Today's Challenge Teacher's Guide

How many hours does Brad spend grooming in a week? Explain your reasoning.

Brad's Daily Schedule Average Time Spent on Activities	
Activity	**Time in Hours**
Eating	$1\frac{3}{5}$
Educational	$7\frac{3}{5}$
Sports and Play	$3\frac{7}{10}$
Sleeping	$8\frac{1}{2}$
Grooming	$\frac{4}{5}$
Other	$1\frac{4}{5}$

TEACHING ACTIONS	GUIDING QUESTIONS	DIFFERENTIATED INSTRUCTION

Before

1. Read the problem.
2. Ask guiding questions.
3. Discuss possible solution strategies.

Make Sense of the Problem

Help students understand the problem:

- What are you asked to find? (How many hours Brad spends grooming in a week)
- How many hours does he spend grooming each day? ($\frac{4}{5}$ hour)
- What else are you asked to do? (Explain how to find the answer)

During

4. Observe students.
5. Ask guiding questions as needed.
6. Have students check if their solutions are reasonable.

Persevere in Solving the Problem

If students need help, ask:

- How many days are in a week? (7)
- What are some ways you can find 7 times $\frac{4}{5}$? (Sample answer: Draw fraction strips; draw a number line)
- What addition equation can you write to help find the answer? (Sample answer: $\frac{4}{5} + \frac{4}{5} + \frac{4}{5} + \frac{4}{5} + \frac{4}{5} + \frac{4}{5} + \frac{4}{5} = n$)

SOLUTION Brad spends $5\frac{3}{5}$ hours grooming in a week; $7 \times \frac{4}{5} = \frac{28}{5} = 5\frac{3}{5}$.

Extra Support

If students have trouble finding the solution, suggest that they draw a model. Have students draw 7 rectangles and divide each into 5 equal parts. Then have the students shade 4 parts in each of the 7 rectangles.

After

7. Discuss the solution.
8. Discuss how to check if the solution is reasonable.
9. Give the problem an extension as needed.

Check the Answer

Ask: Should the answer be greater than or less than 7 hours? How do you know? (Less than 7 hours; Brad spends less than 1 hour each day grooming, so he will spend less than 7 hours in 7 days.)

Discuss whether students answered the right question. If 4 is given for the answer, students found the number of hours he spends grooming in a school week, 5 days, not in 7 days.

Extension

Say: During his 8-day vacation, Brad spent twice as much time playing sports every day as he usually plays sports. How many hours did Brad play sports during his vacation? Explain. ($59\frac{1}{5}$ hours; $3\frac{7}{10} \times 8 = 29\frac{3}{5}$; $29\frac{3}{5} \times 2 = 59\frac{1}{5}$)

How many hours a day does an elephant sleep? Explain your reasoning.

Average Sleep Time	
Animal	**Part of a 24-Hour Day**
Brown bat	$\frac{5}{6}$
Cat	$\frac{1}{2}$
Elephant	$\frac{1}{6}$
Giraffe	$\frac{1}{12}$
Horse	$\frac{1}{8}$
Sloth	$\frac{5}{12}$
Tiger	$\frac{2}{3}$

TEACHING ACTIONS	GUIDING QUESTIONS	DIFFERENTIATED INSTRUCTION

TEACHING ACTIONS

Before
1. Read the problem.
2. Ask guiding questions.
3. Discuss possible solution strategies.

During
4. Observe students.
5. Ask guiding questions as needed.
6. Have students check if their solutions are reasonable.

After
7. Discuss the solution.
8. Discuss how to check if the solution is reasonable.
9. Give the problem an extension as needed.

GUIDING QUESTIONS

Make Sense of the Problem
Help students understand the problem:
- What information are you given? (A table showing the fractional part of a day that animals sleep)
- What are you asked to find? (The number of hours per day that an elephant sleeps)
- What else are you asked to do? (Explain how I found my answer)

Persevere in Solving the Problem
If students need help, ask:
- What part of a 24-hour day does an elephant sleep? ($\frac{1}{6}$)
- What operation do you use to find a fractional part of a number? (Multiplication)
- What fraction is $24 \times \frac{1}{6}$ equal to? ($\frac{24}{6}$)

SOLUTION An elephant sleeps $\frac{1}{6}$ of a 24-hour day; $\frac{1}{6} \times 24 = \frac{24}{6} = 4$; An elephant sleeps 4 hours per day.

Check the Answer
Ask: Multiplying by $\frac{1}{6}$ gives you the same result as dividing by what number? (6)

To check if their solutions are reasonable, ask students to multiply their answer by 6. Since their answer is $\frac{1}{6}$ of 24, they should arrive at 24.

DIFFERENTIATED INSTRUCTION

Vocabulary Review
Review the meaning of *renaming* a fraction. First, illustrate how $\frac{1}{6} \times 24 = \frac{24}{6}$. Say: To rename $\frac{24}{6}$, you divide the numerator by the denominator. So, $\frac{24}{6} = 4$.

Extra Support
If students have trouble finding the solution, suggest that they use counters. Have them use 24 counters to represent 24 hours. Then have them divide the counters into 6 equal groups.

Extension
Say: Suppose a baby elephant sleeps $2\frac{1}{4}$ times as many hours per day as an adult elephant. How many hours per day does a baby elephant sleep? (9 hours)

Use data in the table to write a problem that could be solved with the equation. Then solve the problem.

$$\frac{2}{3} \times 24 = n$$

Average Sleep Time	
Animal	**Part of a 24-Hour Day**
Brown bat	$\frac{5}{6}$
Cat	$\frac{1}{2}$
Elephant	$\frac{1}{6}$
Giraffe	$\frac{1}{12}$
Horse	$\frac{1}{8}$
Sloth	$\frac{5}{12}$
Tiger	$\frac{2}{3}$

TEACHING ACTIONS	GUIDING QUESTIONS	DIFFERENTIATED INSTRUCTION
Before 1. Read the problem. 2. Ask guiding questions. 3. Discuss possible solution strategies.	**Make Sense of the Problem** Help students understand the problem: • What data will you use? (The data in the table) • What are you asked to do? (Write a problem that could be solved with the equation shown, and then solve the problem.)	
During 4. Observe students. 5. Ask guiding questions as needed. 6. Have students check if their solutions are reasonable.	**Persevere in Solving the Problem** If students need help, ask: • How do you read the equation $\frac{2}{3} \times 24 = n$? (Sample answer: Two-thirds of 24 is what number?) • Which animal in the table sleeps $\frac{2}{3}$ of a day? (Tiger) • What equation would you write to find the number of hours per day that a tiger sleeps? (Sample answer: The given equation, $\frac{2}{3} \times 24 = n$.)	**ELL Support** Make sure all students understand how to read equations that include variables. Write $40 \div n = 5$ and $\frac{1}{6} \times 12 = t$. Have students listen and repeat: 40 divided by what number is 5? $\frac{1}{6}$ of 12 is what number?

> **SOLUTION** Sample answer: How many hours per day does a tiger sleep? $\frac{2}{3} \times 24 = 16$; A tiger sleeps 16 hours per day.

TEACHING ACTIONS	GUIDING QUESTIONS	DIFFERENTIATED INSTRUCTION
After 7. Discuss the solution. 8. Discuss how to check if the solution is reasonable. 9. Give the problem an extension as needed.	**Check the Answer** Ask: Should the answer be greater than or less than 12? How do you know? (Sample answer: Greater than 12; Since $\frac{2}{3}$ is more than half, you know that a tiger sleeps more than 12 hours or half the day.) To check if their solutions are reasonable, ask students to find $\frac{1}{3}$ of 24 and add that number to their answer. The sum should be 24. If needed, explain to students that $\frac{1}{3}$ of a day and $\frac{2}{3}$ of a day are 1 whole day, which is 24 hours.	**Extension** Say: Using information in the table, write a problem that could be solved with this equation: $\frac{11}{12} \times 48 = n$. (Sample answer: How many hours is a giraffe awake in a two-day period?)

Today's Challenge Teacher's Guide

How much more of a day does a tiger sleep than an elephant and sloth combined? Explain your reasoning.

Average Sleep Time

Animal	Part of a 24-Hour Day
Brown bat	$\frac{5}{6}$
Cat	$\frac{1}{2}$
Elephant	$\frac{1}{6}$
Giraffe	$\frac{1}{12}$
Horse	$\frac{1}{8}$
Sloth	$\frac{5}{12}$
Tiger	$\frac{2}{3}$

TEACHING ACTIONS	GUIDING QUESTIONS	DIFFERENTIATED INSTRUCTION

Before

1. Read the problem.
2. Ask guiding questions.
3. Discuss possible solution strategies.

Make Sense of the Problem

Help students understand the problem:

- What are you asked to find? (How much more of a day a tiger sleeps than an elephant and sloth combined)
- What part of a day does a tiger sleep? ($\frac{2}{3}$)
- What else are you asked to do? (Explain how I found my answer)

Vocabulary Review

Review the term *common denominator*. Ask students to find a common denominator for $\frac{1}{4}$ and $\frac{3}{8}$. (Sample answer: 8)

During

4. Observe students.
5. Ask guiding questions as needed.
6. Have students check if their solutions are reasonable.

Persevere in Solving the Problem

If students need help, ask:

- How can you find the part of the day that an elephant and sloth sleep combined? (Add $\frac{1}{6}$ and $\frac{5}{12}$) What is a common denominator of $\frac{1}{6}$ and $\frac{5}{12}$? (Sample answer: 12)
- What operation will you use to find how much more of a day a tiger sleeps than an elephant and sloth combined? (Sample answer: Subtraction)
- What is a common denominator of $\frac{2}{3}$ and $\frac{7}{12}$? (Sample answer: 12)

SOLUTION Find the total hours of sleep for the elephant and sloth: $\frac{1}{6} + \frac{5}{12} = \frac{2}{12} + \frac{5}{12} = \frac{7}{12}$; Subtract that from the part of the day a tiger sleeps: $\frac{2}{3} - \frac{7}{12} = \frac{8}{12} - \frac{7}{12} = \frac{1}{12}$; A tiger sleeps $\frac{1}{12}$ of a day more.

Extra Support

Guide students to see that they will need to add and subtract to solve the problem. Students will need to find a common denominator for two different pairs of fractions.

After

7. Discuss the solution.
8. Discuss how to check if the solution is reasonable.
9. Give the problem an extension as needed.

Check the Answer

Ask: Why is it important to find the total for the elephant and sloth first? (Sample answer: You need to find how much longer a tiger sleeps than those two animals combined.)

To check if their solutions are reasonable, ask students to add their answer to the parts of a day that the elephant and sloth sleep combined. The sum should be $\frac{2}{3}$, the part of the day that the tiger sleeps.

Extension

Ask: What part of a day does an elephant sleep? How many hours per week does an elephant sleep? ($\frac{1}{6}$; 28 hours)

Today's Challenge Teacher's Guide

The armadillo sleeps about 3 times the number of hours as the elephant and the giraffe combined. How many hours does an armadillo sleep per day? Explain how to find the answer.

Average Sleep Time	
Animal	**Part of a 24-Hour Day**
Brown bat	$\frac{5}{6}$
Cat	$\frac{1}{2}$
Elephant	$\frac{1}{6}$
Giraffe	$\frac{1}{12}$
Horse	$\frac{1}{8}$
Sloth	$\frac{5}{12}$
Tiger	$\frac{2}{3}$

TEACHING ACTIONS	GUIDING QUESTIONS	DIFFERENTIATED INSTRUCTION
Before 1. Read the problem. 2. Ask guiding questions. 3. Discuss possible solution strategies.	**Make Sense of the Problem** Help students understand the problem: • How long does an armadillo sleep? (About 3 times as long as an elephant and a giraffe combined) • What are you asked to find? (The number of hours an armadillo sleeps per day)	
During 4. Observe students. 5. Ask guiding questions as needed. 6. Have students check if their solutions are reasonable.	**Persevere in Solving the Problem** If students need help, ask: • How can you find the number of hours per day that an elephant sleeps? ($\frac{1}{6} \times 24$) • How many hours per day does a giraffe sleep? (2) • How can you find about how many hours per day an armadillo sleeps? (Add the number of hours per day an elephant sleeps to the number of hours per day a giraffe sleeps. Then multiply this sum by 3.) **SOLUTION** $\frac{1}{6} \times 24 = 4$; $\frac{1}{12} \times 24 = 2$; $4 + 2 = 6$; $3 \times 6 = 18$; An armadillo sleeps about 18 hours per day.	**Extra Support** If students are having difficulty finding the solution, encourage them to draw a picture. Have students draw 3 elephants and 3 giraffes and write the number of hours of sleep per day next to each animal. Then have students add all six numbers.
After 7. Discuss the solution. 8. Discuss how to check if the solution is reasonable. 9. Give the problem an extension as needed.	**Check the Answer** Ask: Why should the answer be less than 24? (There are 24 hours in one day.) To check if their solutions are reasonable, ask students to divide their answer by 3, which will give them the number of hours of sleep per day for the giraffe and the elephant combined. If they subtract the number of hours a giraffe sleeps each day, the result should be the number of hours an elephant sleeps each day.	**Extension** Say: Suppose Caroline sleeps 3 times as many hours a day as a horse. How many hours will Caroline sleep in the month of September? Explain. (270 hours; $\frac{1}{8} \times 24 = 3$; $3 \times 3 = 9$; $9 \times 30 = 270$)

Cats take many short naps throughout the day. If a cat sleeps $\frac{1}{3}$ of an hour at a time, how many short naps does it take? Explain how to find the answer.

Average Sleep Time

Animal	Part of a 24-Hour Day
Brown bat	$\frac{5}{6}$
Cat	$\frac{1}{2}$
Elephant	$\frac{1}{6}$
Giraffe	$\frac{1}{12}$
Horse	$\frac{1}{8}$
Sloth	$\frac{5}{12}$
Tiger	$\frac{2}{3}$

TEACHING ACTIONS	GUIDING QUESTIONS	DIFFERENTIATED INSTRUCTION

Before

1. Read the problem.
2. Ask guiding questions.
3. Discuss possible solution strategies.

Make Sense of the Problem

Help students understand the problem:

- How long is each short nap or "catnap"? ($\frac{1}{3}$ hour)
- What part of a day does a cat sleep? ($\frac{1}{2}$)
- What are you asked to find? (The number of naps a cat takes in one day)

Vocabulary Review

Review the meaning of the term *unit fraction*. Remind students that a unit fraction has a numerator of 1.

During

4. Observe students.
5. Ask guiding questions as needed.
6. Have students check if their solutions are reasonable.

Persevere in Solving the Problem

If students need help, ask:

- What equation can you write to find the number of hours a cat sleeps each day? (Sample answer: $\frac{1}{2} \times 24 = n$)
- What operation can you use to find how many $\frac{1}{3}$ hours are in 12 hours? (Sample answer: Division)
- How do you divide by a unit fraction? (Multiply by the denominator of the unit fraction)

SOLUTION A cat takes 36 catnaps per day. Sample answer: Find the number of hours a cat sleeps per day: $\frac{1}{2} \times 24 = 12$ hours. Find the number of $\frac{1}{3}$ hours in 12 hours: $12 \div \frac{1}{3} = 12 \times 3 = 36$.

Extra Support

If students are having difficulty finding the solution, suggest that they approach the problem in a different way. Have them find the number of $\frac{1}{3}$ hours in 1 hour. Then have them multiply that number by the number of hours a cat sleeps per day, 12.

After

7. Discuss the solution.
8. Discuss how to check if the solution is reasonable.
9. Give the problem an extension as needed.

Check the Answer

Ask: Why is it important to find the number of hours a cat sleeps per day first? (Sample answer: You need to find how many $\frac{1}{3}$ hours are in that number of hours.)

To check if their solutions are reasonable, ask students to divide their answer by 12. The result will be the number of catnaps in 1 hour, which should be 3.

Extension

Say: Suppose a tiger sleeps $2\frac{1}{2}$ hours straight during the night. The rest of the day, it takes 45-minute naps. How many naps does it take each day? (18)

Today's Challenge Teacher's Guide

What are the dimensions of a photograph in feet? Remember, there are 12 inches in 1 foot. Explain how to find the answer.

Traveling Exhibit Information

Featured art	40 photographs
Size of each photograph	36 in. by 48 in. (91 cm by 122 cm)
Storage	8 crates
Size of each crate	42 in. by 54 in. by 36 in. (107 cm by 137 cm by 91 cm)
Total weight	2,000 pounds (908 kg)

TEACHING ACTIONS	GUIDING QUESTIONS	DIFFERENTIATED INSTRUCTION
Before 1. Read the problem. 2. Ask guiding questions. 3. Discuss possible solution strategies.	**Make Sense of the Problem** Help students understand the problem: • What information are you given? (Sample answer: Information such as the size of photographs) • What are you asked to find? (The dimensions of a photograph in feet) • What else do you need to do? (Explain how to find my answer)	**Vocabulary Review** Discuss the meaning of *dimensions* with students. Point out that the measurements for length and width are the dimensions for two-dimensional objects, such as a piece of paper. For three-dimensional objects, the measurements given for length, width, and height are the dimensions.
During 4. Observe students. 5. Ask guiding questions as needed. 6. Have students check if their solutions are reasonable.	**Persevere in Solving the Problem** If students need help, ask: • In what two units are the dimensions of each photograph given? (Inches and centimeters) • Which dimensions should you use to solve the problem? Why? (36 inches by 48 inches; Because I need to give the answer in feet, and it is easy to change from inches to feet) • How can you find the dimensions of the photograph in feet? (Divide the dimensions given in inches by 12.) **SOLUTION** The dimensions of a photograph are 3 feet by 4 feet. Sample answer: To change from inches to feet, I can divide each dimension in inches by 12: $36 \div 12 = 3$; $48 \div 12 = 4$.	**Extra Support** If students have trouble understanding that they need to divide by 12, have them mark the dimensions in inches on a number line. Then, have them mark every 12 inches to show each foot.
After 7. Discuss the solution. 8. Discuss how to check if the solution is reasonable. 9. Give the problem an extension as needed.	**Check the Answer** Ask: Should the answers be less than or greater than the dimensions in inches? Why? (Sample answer: Less than; Inches are smaller than feet so the number of feet will be less than the number of inches.) To check if their solutions are reasonable, ask students to multiply their dimensions in feet by 12. Ask: Are the products equal to the dimensions in inches? (Yes; $3 \times 12 = 36$; $4 \times 12 = 48$)	**Extension** Say: Another photograph is 30 inches by 45 inches. What are the dimensions of the photograph in feet? Explain how to find the answer. (The dimensions of the photograph are 2.5 feet by 3.75 feet. Sample answer: To change from inches to feet, divide by 12: $30 \div 12 = 2.5$; $45 \div 12 = 3.75$.)

How much longer or wider is the crate than a photograph? Give your answer in inches and in fractions of a foot. Explain how to find the answer.

Traveling Exhibit Information

Featured art	40 photographs
Size of each photograph	36 in. by 48 in. (91 cm by 122 cm)
Storage	8 crates
Size of each crate	42 in. by 54 in. by 36 in. (107 cm by 137 cm by 91 cm)
Total weight	2,000 pounds (908 kg)

TEACHING ACTIONS	GUIDING QUESTIONS	DIFFERENTIATED INSTRUCTION
Before 1. Read the problem. 2. Ask guiding questions. 3. Discuss possible solution strategies.	**Make Sense of the Problem** Help students understand the problem: • What are you asked to find? (How much longer or wider a crate is than a photograph) • How will you give your answer? (In inches and in fractions of a foot) • What else are you asked to do? (Explain how to find the answer)	**Vocabulary Review** Review the terms *inch*, *foot*, and *yard*. Remind students that there are 12 inches in 1 foot and 3 feet in 1 yard. These are customary units.
During 4. Observe students. 5. Ask guiding questions as needed. 6. Have students check if their solutions are reasonable.	**Persevere in Solving the Problem** If students need help, ask: • What is the width of a crate in inches? (42 inches) What is the width of a photograph in inches? (36 inches) • What is the length of a crate in inches? (54 inches) What is the length of a photograph in inches? (48 inches) • What words in the question tell you that you could subtract? (How much longer or wider) • What fraction of a foot is 6 inches? ($\frac{6}{12}$ or $\frac{1}{2}$) **SOLUTION** Students should find that the crate is 6 inches ($\frac{1}{2}$ foot) wider or 6 inches ($\frac{1}{2}$ foot) longer than the photograph. Sample answer: $42 - 36 = 6$ inches; 6 inches is $\frac{6}{12}$ of a foot; $\frac{6}{12} = \frac{1}{2}$; $54 - 48 = 6$ inches.	**ELL Support** To check understanding, ask students to repeat and complete the following sentence frames: There are 24 _____ in 2 _____. (inches; feet) 3 _____ is the same length as 36 _____. (feet; inches)
After 7. Discuss the solution. 8. Discuss how to check if the solution is reasonable. 9. Give the problem an extension as needed.	**Check the Answer** Ask: Why would you subtract inches first and then change to feet? (Sample answer: It is easier to subtract 36 from 42 or 48 from 54 and then change 6 inches to feet.) To check if their solutions are reasonable, ask students to add their answer in inches to the width or length of the photograph. The sum should be the width or length of the crate.	**Extension** Say: Suppose there are art prints the same length and width as a photograph. Each print is $\frac{1}{4}$ inch thick. Crates can be packed $\frac{4}{5}$ full. How many prints can be stacked in one crate? Explain. (115 prints can be stacked in one crate; $\frac{4}{5} \times 36 = 28.8$; $28.8 \div 0.25 = 115.2$)

Today's Challenge Teacher's Guide

Each wall has 5 photographs. What is the total amount of wall space the 5 photographs cover, in square feet? Explain how to find the answer, including how to use the formula for the area of a rectangle.

Traveling Exhibit Information

Featured art	40 photographs
Size of each photograph	36 in. by 48 in. (91 cm by 122 cm)
Storage	8 crates
Size of each crate	42 in. by 54 in. by 36 in. (107 cm by 137 cm by 91 cm)
Total weight	2,000 pounds (908 kg)

TEACHING ACTIONS	GUIDING QUESTIONS	DIFFERENTIATED INSTRUCTION

Before

1. Read the problem.
2. Ask guiding questions.
3. Discuss possible solution strategies.

Make Sense of the Problem

Help students understand the problem:

- How many photographs are on each wall? (5)
- What are you asked to find? (The total amount of wall space that the photographs cover)
- What unit will you use for your answer? (Square feet)
- What else are you asked to do? (Explain how to find the answer and how to use the formula for the area of a rectangle)

Vocabulary Review

Ask students to define the term *area* in their own words. Ask for real-world examples of when students might need to find area.

During

4. Observe students.
5. Ask guiding questions as needed.
6. Have students check if their solutions are reasonable.

Persevere in Solving the Problem

If students need help, ask:

- What are the dimensions of a photograph, in inches? (36 in. by 48 in.)
- How can you change each of the dimensions from inches to feet? (Divide by 12)
- What is the formula for the area of a rectangle? ($A = \ell \times w$)
- How can you find the wall space that 1 photograph covers? 5 photographs? (1 photograph: Multiply the length times the width; 5 photographs: Multiply the area of 1 photograph by 5)

SOLUTION 5 photographs cover 60 square feet of wall space; Sample answer: Change inches to feet: $36 \div 12 = 3$; $48 \div 12 = 4$; $A = \ell \times w$, so $A = 4 \times 3 = 12$ sq ft. Then find the area for 5 photographs: $5 \times 12 = 60$ sq ft.

Extra Support

If students are having difficulty finding the solution, suggest that they draw a picture. Have them draw 5 photographs hung on a wall. Then have students label the dimensions of each photograph in feet.

After

7. Discuss the solution.
8. Discuss how to check if the solution is reasonable.
9. Give the problem an extension as needed.

Check the Answer

Ask: How do you know that 36 and 48 will divide evenly by 12? (Sample answer: They are multiples of 12.)

Discuss whether students answered the right question. If 8,640 is given for the answer, students found the total area in square inches, not in square feet.

Extension

Say: Find the answer to this problem again but in square inches instead of square feet. Explain how to find the answer. (8,640 square inches; The area of one picture = $36 \times 48 = 1,728$ sq in.; $1,728 \times 5 = 8,640$ sq in.)

Each crate and padding has a mass of 24 kilograms, before the photos are put in. What is the mass of each photograph in kilograms? Explain how to find the answer.

Traveling Exhibit Information	
Featured art	40 photographs
Size of each photograph	36 in. by 48 in. (91 cm by 122 cm)
Storage	8 crates
Size of each crate	42 in. by 54 in. by 36 in. (107 cm by 137 cm by 91 cm)
Total weight	2,000 pounds (908 kg)

TEACHING ACTIONS	GUIDING QUESTIONS	DIFFERENTIATED INSTRUCTION
Before 1. Read the problem. 2. Ask guiding questions. 3. Discuss possible solution strategies.	**Make Sense of the Problem** Help students understand the problem: • What is the mass of each crate with padding before the photographs are put in? (24 kg) • Where can you find the total mass of all the crates? (In the *Traveling Exhibit Information*) • What are you asked to find? (The mass of each photograph in kilograms)	
During 4. Observe students. 5. Ask guiding questions as needed. 6. Have students check for reasonableness.	**Persevere in Solving the Problem** If students need help, ask: • How many crates are given? (8) • How can you find the mass of one crate with photographs? (Divide the total mass by 8) How can you find the mass of the photographs in one crate? (Subtract the mass of one crate without the photographs from the mass of one crate with the photographs) • What expression can you write to find the number of photographs in one crate? (40 photographs ÷ 8 crates) **SOLUTION** Each photograph has a mass of 17.9 kilograms; Sample answer: Mass of one crate: $908 ÷ 8 = 113.5$ kg; Mass of photographs in one crate: $113.5 - 24 = 89.5$ kg; Each crate has 5 photographs: $40 ÷ 8 = 5$; Mass of 1 photograph: $89.5 ÷ 5 = 17.9$ kg)	**ELL Support** Rephrase the problem for students who need extra language support. For example, you might say: The mass of a crate without photographs is 24 kilograms. What is the mass of each photograph from a full crate?
After 7. Discuss the solution. 8. Discuss how to check if the solution is reasonable. 9. Give the problem an extension as needed.	**Check the Answer** Ask: Why is it important to know the number of photographs in one crate? (Sample answer: You can find the mass of all of the photographs in 1 crate, and then find the mass of 1 photograph.) Discuss whether students answered the right question. If 89.5 kilograms is given for the answer, students found the mass of the photographs in 1 crate, not the mass of 1 photograph.	**Extension** Say: For another exhibit, there are 7 crates. There are 35 photographs with an equal number in each crate. What is the total mass of the 7 crates in kilograms? (Seven crates have a mass of 794.5 kilograms.

Today's Challenge Teacher's Guide

What is the volume of a crate? Explain how to find the answer, including how to use the formula for the volume of a rectangular prism.

Traveling Exhibit Information

Featured art	40 photographs
Size of each photograph	36 in. by 48 in. (91 cm by 122 cm)
Storage	8 crates
Size of each crate	42 in. by 54 in. by 36 in. (107 cm by 137 cm by 91 cm)
Total weight	2,000 pounds (908 kg)

TEACHING ACTIONS	GUIDING QUESTIONS	DIFFERENTIATED INSTRUCTION
Before 1. Read the problem. 2. Ask guiding questions. 3. Discuss possible solution strategies.	**Make Sense of the Problem** Help students understand the problem: • What are you asked to find? (The volume of a crate) • What else are you asked to do? (Explain how to find the answer and use the formula) • What formula will you use? (The formula for the volume of a rectangular prism)	**Vocabulary Review** Review the term *cubic units*. Show students a unit cube and remind them that the volume of a rectangular prism is the number of unit cubes that will fill it, expressed in cubic units. The units in this problem are expressed in inches and in centimeters.
During 4. Observe students. 5. Ask guiding questions as needed. 6. Have students check if their solutions are reasonable.	**Persevere in Solving the Problem** If students need help, ask: • What are the dimension of a crate? (42 in. by 54 in. by 36 in. or 107 cm by 137 cm by 91 cm) • What is the formula for the volume of a rectangular prism? (Sample answer: $V = \ell \times w \times h$) • Which unit will you use for the volume of the crate? (Sample answer: Cubic inches) **SOLUTION** Volume of a crate: 81,648 cubic inches. Sample answer: $V = \ell \times w \times h$, so $V = 42 \times 54 \times 36 = 81{,}648$ cubic inches.	**ELL Support** Break down the term *rectangular prism* into the two words *rectangular* and *prism*. Tell students that a *rectangular prism* is a prism that has two identical bases in the shape of a rectangle. Demonstrate with a rectangular box, pointing out the rectangular bases of the prism.
After 7. Discuss the solution. 8. Discuss how to check if the solution is reasonable. 9. Give the problem an extension as needed.	**Check the Answer** Ask: What is another way to write the formula for the volume of a rectangular prism? (Sample answer: $V = B \times h$) To check if their solutions are reasonable, ask students to divide their answer by the height of the crate. Students should find that the answer is the area of the base of the crate.	**Extension** Say: Suppose there is a crate that is 2 inches longer, wider, and taller. How much more, in cubic inches, does the larger crate hold? Explain. (11,984 cubic inches more; $42 + 2 = 44$; $54 + 2 = 56$; $36 + 2 = 38$; $44 \times 56 \times 38 = 93{,}632$; $93{,}632 - 81{,}648 = 11{,}984$)

Jaime created a model of the sedimentary layers of the Grand Canyon. He glued a piece of string around the glass prism between the Tapeats Sandstone layer and the Vishnu Schist layer to show where there is an unconformity. How long did Jaime have to cut the string so it would fit perfectly around the glass? Show how to use a formula to find the length of the string.

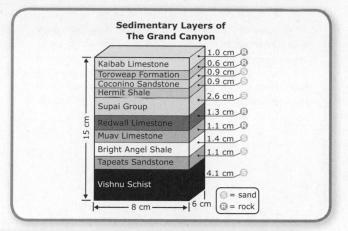

Sedimentary Layers of The Grand Canyon

Kaibab Limestone	1.0 cm Ⓡ
Toroweap Formation	0.6 cm Ⓡ
Coconino Sandstone	0.9 cm Ⓢ
Hermit Shale	0.9 cm Ⓢ
Supai Group	2.6 cm Ⓢ
Redwall Limestone	1.3 cm Ⓡ
Muav Limestone	1.1 cm Ⓡ
Bright Angel Shale	1.4 cm Ⓢ
Tapeats Sandstone	1.1 cm Ⓢ
Vishnu Schist	4.1 cm Ⓢ

15 cm — 8 cm — 6 cm

Ⓢ = sand Ⓡ = rock

TEACHING ACTIONS	GUIDING QUESTIONS	DIFFERENTIATED INSTRUCTION
Before 1. Read the problem. 2. Ask guiding questions. 3. Discuss possible solution strategies.	**Make Sense of the Problem** Help students understand the problem: • Where did Jaime glue the piece of string? (Around the glass prism between two layers) • What are you asked to find? (The length of string that would fit perfectly around the glass) • What are you asked to show? (How to use a formula to find the length of the string)	**Vocabulary Review** Review the term *formula*. Ask students for examples of formulas they know, such as how to find the perimeter or area of a rectangle.
During 4. Observe students. 5. Ask guiding questions as needed. 6. Have students check if their solutions are reasonable.	**Persevere in Solving the Problem** If students need help, ask: • Once Jaime glued the string in place, what shape did the string make? (A rectangle) • What is the formula for the perimeter of a rectangle? ($P = 2\ell + 2w$) • Which dimensions in the diagram are the length and width of the rectangle made by the string? (8 cm and 6 cm)	**Extra Support** If students have trouble finding the solution, suggest that they use a model to help them answer the question. Pair students, and provide each pair with an example of a rectangular prism, such as a tissue box. Ask students to wrap a string around their prisms the same way Jaime did with his prism.
	SOLUTION Jaime had to cut the string to measure 28 cm. He used the formula for finding the perimeter of a rectangle: $P = 2\ell + 2w$; $2(8) + 2(6) = 16 + 12 = 28$.	
After 7. Discuss the solution. 8. Discuss how to check if the solution is reasonable. 9. Give the problem an extension as needed.	**Check the Answer** Ask: How do you know which dimensions to use in the diagram? (Sample answer: The string does not wrap around the prism vertically, so the height, 15 cm, is not needed.) Discuss whether students answered the right question. If 42 cm or 46 cm is given for the answer, students found the length of a string wrapped top-to-bottom around the prism.	**Extension** Say: Suppose Jaime wants to protect the glass by putting plastic strips on every edge of the prism. How many centimeters of plastic will he need to cover every edge? Explain. (116 cm; A rectangular prism has 12 edges: 15 + 8 + 15 + 8 + 15 + 8 + 6 + 6 + 6 + 6 = 116 cm)

Jaime covered the 2 sides and the back of the glass prism with dark paper so only the front would show the layers of the sedimentary material. Show how to use a formula to find the area of the back of the glass prism and each side. Jaime has 400 square cm of paper. Does he have enough paper to cover the sides and the back of the prism? Tell how you know.

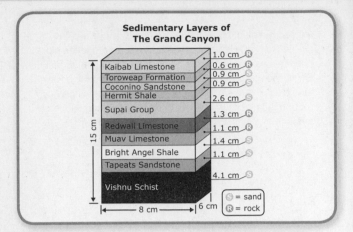

Sedimentary Layers of The Grand Canyon

Kaibab Limestone	1.0 cm Ⓡ
Toroweap Formation	0.6 cm Ⓡ
Coconino Sandstone	0.9 cm Ⓢ
Hermit Shale	0.9 cm Ⓢ
Supai Group	2.6 cm Ⓢ
Redwall Limestone	1.3 cm Ⓡ
Muav Limestone	1.1 cm Ⓡ
Bright Angel Shale	1.4 cm Ⓢ
Tapeats Sandstone	1.1 cm Ⓢ
Vishnu Schist	4.1 cm Ⓢ

15 cm ← → 8 cm → 6 cm

Ⓢ = sand
Ⓡ = rock

TEACHING ACTIONS	GUIDING QUESTIONS	DIFFERENTIATED INSTRUCTION

Before

1. Read the problem.
2. Ask guiding questions.
3. Discuss possible solution strategies.

Make Sense of the Problem

Help students understand the problem:

- What parts of the prism does Jaime want to cover with dark paper? (The 2 sides and the back)
- How much paper does he have? (400 sq cm)
- If you want to find the amount of paper needed to cover a surface, what do you need to find? (The area)

Vocabulary Review

Review the definition of *rectangular prism*. Ask students for examples of everyday objects that are rectangular prisms. Make sure students know where the top, bottom, back, front, and sides of the prism are located.

During

4. Observe students.
5. Ask guiding questions as needed.
6. Have students check if their solutions are reasonable.

Persevere in Solving the Problem

If students need help, ask:

- What is the length of the back of the prism? (15 cm) The width? (8 cm)
- What is the length of one of the sides of the prism? (15 cm) The width? (6 cm)
- What is the formula for the area of a rectangle? ($A = \ell \times w$)

SOLUTION Jaime has enough paper; The formula for area is $A = \ell \times w$. The area of the back: $15 \times 8 = 120$ sq cm; Area of each side: $15 \times 6 = 90$ sq cm; Total area: $120 + 90 + 90 = 300$ sq cm; $400 > 300$.

ELL Support

Break the term *square inch* into the words *square* and *inch*. A square inch is a square with one-inch sides. If the area of a rectangle is 20 square inches, you could take 20 squares, each 1 inch by 1 inch, and cover the rectangle.

After

7. Discuss the solution.
8. Discuss how to check if the solution is reasonable.
9. Give the problem an extension as needed.

Check the Answer

Ask: Why is it important to study the diagram carefully? (Sample answer: The diagram shows which dimensions to use for the back and sides of the prism.)

To check if their solutions are reasonable, ask students to subtract the area of all three surfaces from 400 sq cm. They should have 100 sq cm remaining.

Extension

Say: Suppose Jaime wants to cover the entire prism with dark paper except for a 7-inch square window cut out in the front. How much paper will cover the prism? (467 sq cm; $2 \times ((6 \times 15) + (8 \times 6) + (8 \times 15)) = 2 \times 258 = 516$; $516 - (7 \times 7) = 516 - 49 = 467$ sq cm)

Today's Challenge Teacher's Guide

Develop a formula for finding the volume of any layer of the sedimentary material. Explain the formula and how you found it. Use the formula to find the volume of one layer of your choice.

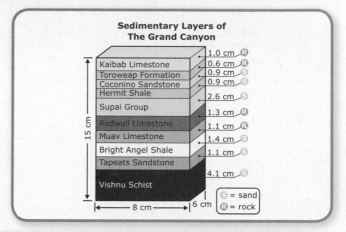

Sedimentary Layers of The Grand Canyon

Kaibab Limestone	1.0 cm Ⓡ
Toroweap Formation	0.6 cm Ⓡ
Coconino Sandstone	0.9 cm Ⓢ
Hermit Shale	0.9 cm Ⓢ
Supai Group	2.6 cm Ⓢ
Redwall Limestone	1.3 cm Ⓡ
Muav Limestone	1.1 cm Ⓡ
Bright Angel Shale	1.4 cm Ⓢ
Tapeats Sandstone	1.1 cm Ⓢ
Vishnu Schist	4.1 cm Ⓢ

15 cm · 8 cm · 6 cm

Ⓢ = sand   Ⓡ = rock

TEACHING ACTIONS	GUIDING QUESTIONS	DIFFERENTIATED INSTRUCTION
Before 1. Read the problem. 2. Ask guiding questions. 3. Discuss possible solution strategies.	**Make Sense of the Problem** Help students understand the problem: • What are you asked to develop? (A formula for finding the volume of any layer in the rectangular prism) • After you develop the formula, what will you use it to find? (The volume of a chosen layer of sedimentary material)	**Vocabulary Review** Explain that *volume* is the number of *cubic units* needed to fill a solid figure. Review the formula for finding the volume of a rectangular prism with students: $V = \ell \times w \times h$.
During 4. Observe students. 5. Ask guiding questions as needed. 6. Have students check if their solutions are reasonable.	**Persevere in Solving the Problem** If students need help, ask: • What is the length of one of the layers in the prism? (Sample answer: The length of the Kaibab Limestone layer is 8 cm.) • What is the width of the layer you chose? (Sample answer: The width of the Kaibab Limestone layer is 6 cm.) What is its height? (1 cm) • What formula and dimensions will you use to find the volume of your chosen layer? ($V = \ell \times w \times h$; Dimensions for the Kaibab Limestone layer are 8 cm, 6 cm, and 1 cm.) **SOLUTION** Sample answer: $V = \ell \times w \times h$ or $V = B \times h$, so the volume of the Kaibab Limestone layer is $V = 8 \times 6 \times 1$ or $48 \times 1 = 48$ cu cm. I multiplied the length by the width by the height to get the volume.	**Extra Support** If students struggle with the problem and solution, encourage them to use unit cubes to review the concept of volume. Have them build rectangular prisms of different sizes, counting the cubes used in each one.
After 7. Discuss the solution. 8. Discuss how to check if the solution is reasonable. 9. Give the problem an extension as needed.	**Check the Answer** Ask: Why is it important to know the formula for the volume of a prism? (Sample answer: You can begin with the formula and then substitute the numbers for the dimensions of the prism. You can multiply the numbers in any order.) Ask: Is it reasonable that the volume of the Kaibab Limestone layer is 48 cu cm? Explain. (Yes; Sample answer: Since the height is only 1 cm, the volume is the product of 8×6, which is the same as the product of $8 \times 6 \times 1$.)	**Extension** Say: Suppose Jaime ships his prism in a padded box that fits snugly around the prism. The padding is 1 cm thick on each side of the prism. What is the volume of just the padding? (640 cu cm; $8 \times 6 \times 15 = 720$; $(8 + 2) \times (6 + 2) \times (15 + 2) = 1,360$; $1,360 - 720 = 640$ cu cm)

Jaime used colored rocks and sand to create the model. What was the total volume of colored rock that he used? Explain how to use one or more formulas to find the answer.

What was the volume of colored sand Jaime used? Explain how to use the total volume of the glass prism to find the total volume of the colored sand Jaime used.

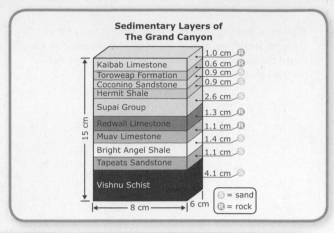

Sedimentary Layers of The Grand Canyon

	1.0 cm R
Kaibab Limestone	0.6 cm R
Toroweap Formation	0.9 cm S
Coconino Sandstone	0.9 cm S
Hermit Shale	
Supai Group	2.6 cm S
Redwall Limestone	1.3 cm R
Muav Limestone	1.1 cm R
Bright Angel Shale	1.4 cm S
Tapeats Sandstone	1.1 cm S
Vishnu Schist	4.1 cm S

15 cm ← → 8 cm ← → 6 cm

S = sand
R = rock

TEACHING ACTIONS	GUIDING QUESTIONS	DIFFERENTIATED INSTRUCTION

Before

1. Read the problem.
2. Ask guiding questions.
3. Discuss possible solution strategies.

Make Sense of the Problem

Help students understand the problem:

- What are you asked to find first? (The total volume of colored rock Jaime used)
- What are you asked to find next? (The total volume of colored sand Jaime used)
- How will you know which layers are rock and which layers are sand? (The key to the right of the model tells me.)

Vocabulary Review

Remind students that the formula for the volume of a rectangular prism, $V = \ell \times w \times h$, can also be written as $V = B \times h$. B is the area of the base, or the length times the width.

During

4. Observe students.
5. Ask guiding questions as needed.
6. Have students check if their solutions are reasonable.

Persevere in Solving the Problem

If students need help, ask:

- What are the heights of the layers of colored rock? (1.0 cm, 0.6 cm, 1.3 cm, and 1.1 cm)
- How can you find the volume of colored rock? (Multiply the base, *B*, by the sum of the heights of the colored rock, or multiply the length by the width by the sum of the heights of the colored rock)
- If you know the total volume of the prism, how can you find the volume of the colored sand? (Subtract the volume of the colored rock)

SOLUTION Colored rock: $1 + 0.6 + 1.3 + 1.1 = 4$; $V = B \times h$: $48 \times 4 = 192$ cu cm. Whole prism: $V = 48 \times 15 = 720$ cu cm; Colored sand: $720 - 192 = 528$ cu cm.

ELL Support

Help students read the problem and break it into more manageable parts. Create a chart on the board, listing the key verbs that students need to know. Focus on *was* in sentences 2 and 4, explaining that in these sentences, it is the main verb, the past tense of the verb *to be*.

After

7. Discuss the solution.
8. Discuss how to check if the solution is reasonable.
9. Give the problem an extension as needed.

Check the Answer

Ask: Why is it helpful to find the total volume of the prism in order to find the volume of the colored sand? (Sample answer: It is easier to subtract the volume of the colored rock from the total volume of the prism than it is to find the volume of each layer of the colored sand.)

To check if their solutions are reasonable, ask students to add their the volume of the colored rock to the volume of the colored sand. The sum should be the total volume of the prism, 720 cu cm.

Extension

Ask: What is the total volume of the Toroweap Formation, Supai Group, and Tapeats Sandstone in Jaime's model? (206.4 cu cm; $0.6 + 2.6 + 1.1 = 4.3$; $48 \times 4.3 = 206.4$ cu cm)

Today's Challenge Teacher's Guide

Jaime used 10 different colors of sand and rock for his science project. He bought 1 bag of each color. Each different color of rock came in a 2-ounce bag and each different color of sand came in a 4-ounce bag. How many pounds of rock did Jaime buy? How many pounds of sand did he buy? Explain how to find the answer.

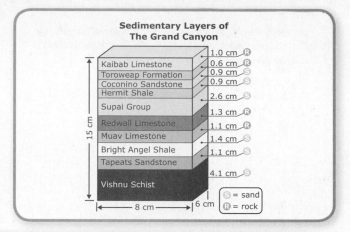

Sedimentary Layers of The Grand Canyon

Kaibab Limestone	1.0 cm ®️
Toroweap Formation	0.6 cm ®️
Coconino Sandstone	0.9 cm ⓢ
Hermit Shale	0.9 cm ⓢ
Supai Group	2.6 cm ⓢ
Redwall Limestone	1.3 cm ®️
Muav Limestone	1.1 cm ®️
Bright Angel Shale	1.4 cm ⓢ
Tapeats Sandstone	1.1 cm ⓢ
Vishnu Schist	4.1 cm ⓢ

15 cm · 8 cm · 6 cm

ⓢ = sand ®️ = rock

TEACHING ACTIONS	GUIDING QUESTIONS	DIFFERENTIATED INSTRUCTION

Before

1. Read the problem.
2. Ask guiding questions.
3. Discuss possible solution strategies.

Make Sense of the Problem

Help students understand the problem:

- How many bags of sand and rock did Jaime buy? (1 bag of each color)
- How many ounces are in each bag of colored rock? (2 oz) In each bag of colored sand? (4 oz)
- What are you asked to find? (The number of pounds of rock and sand Jaime bought)

Vocabulary Review

Review the conversion of *ounces* to *pounds*. Remind students that 16 ounces equals 1 pound.

During

4. Observe students.
5. Ask guiding questions as needed.
6. Have students check if their solutions are reasonable.

Persevere in Solving the Problem

If students need help, ask:

- How many layers of colored rock does Jaime have in his prism? (4)
- How many layers of colored sand does Jaime have in his prism? (6)
- How can you find how many pounds of colored rock Jaime bought? (Sample answer: Multiply 4 layers of colored rock × 2 ounces for each layer = 8 ounces. If I divide 8 by 16, I get $\frac{1}{2}$ total pound of colored rock.)

SOLUTION 4 bags of colored rock, 4 × 2 oz = 8 oz. I know that 1 lb = 16 oz, so I found 8 ÷ 16 = $\frac{1}{2}$ pound of colored rock. 6 bags of colored sand, 6 × 4 oz = 24 oz. I found 24 ÷ 16 = $1\frac{8}{16}$ or $1\frac{1}{2}$ pounds of colored sand.

ELL Support

Provide these sentence frames for students to complete as a way to state their answers:

Jaime bought 8 _____ of colored rock, which is equal to _____ pound. (ounces; $\frac{1}{2}$)

He bought 24 _____ of colored sand, which is equal to _____ pounds. (ounces; $1\frac{1}{2}$)

After

7. Discuss the solution.
8. Discuss how to check if the solution is reasonable.
9. Give the problem an extension as needed.

Check the Answer

Ask: Why do you divide both numbers by 16? (Because there are 16 ounces in 1 pound and I need to convert the ounces I found to pounds)

Discuss if their solutions are reasonable. If 8 and 24 are given for the answers, students found the number of ounces of rock and sand that Jaime bought, but they did not finish the problem by finding the number of pounds he bought.

Extension

Say: Colored sand costs $0.49 per ounce, and colored rock costs $1.12 per ounce. How much did Jaime pay in all for the colored sand and rock? ($20.72; $0.49 × 24 oz = $11.76; $1.12 × 8 oz = $8.96; $11.76 + $8.96 = $20.72)

How many elephants were born at the reserve? What is the most common height of the elephants born at the reserve? Explain how you know.

Heights of Elephants Born at Reserve (rounded to the nearest quarter foot)

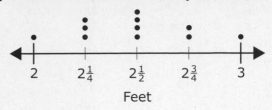

Feet

TEACHING ACTIONS	GUIDING QUESTIONS	DIFFERENTIATED INSTRUCTION
Before 1. Read the problem. 2. Ask guiding questions. 3. Discuss possible solution strategies.	**Make Sense of the Problem** Help students understand the problem: • What are you asked to find? (How many elephants were born at the reserve and the most common height of the elephants) • What data are shown in the line plot? (The heights of elephants born at the reserve) • What does each dot on the line plot represent? (The height of one elephant born at the reserve)	**Vocabulary Review** Have students complete this sentence frame: A display of responses along a number line with dots above the responses, to indicate the number of times a response occurred is called a _____ . (line plot)
During 4. Observe students. 5. Ask guiding questions as needed. 6. Have students check if their solutions are reasonable.	**Persevere in Solving the Problem** If students need help, ask: • How will you find the number of elephants born at the reserve? (Count the total number of dots on the line plot) • How will you find the most common height of the elephants? (Find the number of feet that has the most dots above it) **SOLUTION** There were 11 elephants born at the reserve because this is the total number of dots on the line plot. The most common height is $2\frac{1}{2}$ feet because that number of feet has the most dots on the plot.	**Extra Support** If students have trouble understanding how to read the line plot, ask: What do the numbers along the number line show? (The heights of the elephants in feet) What does it mean when there is more than one dot above a number? (There is more than one elephant with the same height.)
After 7. Discuss the solution. 8. Discuss how to check if the solution is reasonable. 9. Give the problem an extension as needed.	**Check the Answer** Ask: What is the greatest number of dots above one number on the line plot? (4) How many times does $2\frac{1}{2}$ feet occur in the line plot? (4 times) Ask students to check their answer for the number of elephants born at the reserve by recounting the number of dots in the line plot.	**Extension** Ask: Are there any outliers in the line plot? Explain. (No; Sample answer: There is no data value that is very different from the other values.)

How many more elephants are $2\frac{1}{2}$ feet or taller than are $2\frac{1}{4}$ feet or shorter? Explain how you know.

Heights of Elephants Born at Reserve (rounded to the nearest quarter foot)

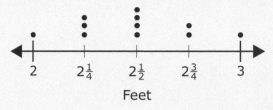

Feet

TEACHING ACTIONS	GUIDING QUESTIONS	DIFFERENTIATED INSTRUCTION
Before 1. Read the problem. 2. Ask guiding questions. 3. Discuss possible solution strategies.	**Make Sense of the Problem** Help students understand the problem: • What are you asked to find? (How many more elephants are $2\frac{1}{2}$ feet or taller than are $2\frac{1}{4}$ feet or shorter) • What heights are shown on the number line? (2 feet, $2\frac{1}{4}$ feet, $2\frac{1}{2}$ feet, $2\frac{3}{4}$ feet, 3 feet)	
During 4. Observe students. 5. Ask guiding questions as needed. 6. Have students check if their solutions are reasonable.	**Persevere in Solving the Problem** If students need help, ask: • How many elephants are $2\frac{1}{2}$ feet or taller? (7) • How many elephants are $2\frac{1}{4}$ feet or shorter? (4) • Which operation will you use to find how many more elephants are $2\frac{1}{2}$ feet or taller than are $2\frac{1}{4}$ feet or shorter? (Subtraction) **SOLUTION** 3 more elephants are $2\frac{1}{2}$ feet or taller than are $2\frac{1}{4}$ feet or shorter. There are 7 heights greater than or equal to $2\frac{1}{2}$ feet and 4 heights less than or equal to $2\frac{1}{4}$ feet. $7 - 4 = 3$	**ELL Support** Point out the words *how many more*. Explain that these words usually indicate that you will need to subtract to solve the problem.
After 7. Discuss the solution. 8. Discuss how to check if the solution is reasonable. 9. Give the problem an extension as needed.	**Check the Answer** Ask: When you found the number of elephants that are $2\frac{1}{2}$ feet or taller, did you include heights that are equal to $2\frac{1}{2}$ feet? (Yes) When you found the number of elephants that are $2\frac{1}{4}$ feet or shorter, did you include heights that are equal to $2\frac{1}{4}$ feet? (Yes) Say: Add the number of heights you found that are $2\frac{1}{2}$ or taller to the number that are $2\frac{1}{4}$ feet or shorter. The sum should equal 11, the total number of elephants born at the reserve.	**Extension** Ask: In the line plot, do any of the data values occur the same number of times? Explain. (Yes; 2 feet and 3 feet both occur one time because there is 1 dot over each of these heights on the line plot.)

Today's Challenge Teacher's Guide

Another baby elephant is born at the reserve. The elephant is 2 feet 4 inches tall. If this height were added to the line plot, how would the line plot change? Explain.

Heights of Elephants Born at Reserve (rounded to the nearest quarter foot)

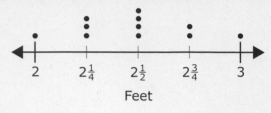

Feet

TEACHING ACTIONS	GUIDING QUESTIONS	DIFFERENTIATED INSTRUCTION
Before 1. Read the problem. 2. Ask guiding questions. 3. Discuss possible solution strategies.	**Make Sense of the Problem** Help students understand the problem: • How tall is the new baby elephant? (2 feet 4 inches tall) • What are you asked to explain? (How adding another height to the line plot would change the line plot) • What statement is given about the heights in the line plot? (The heights are rounded to the nearest quarter foot.)	
During 4. Observe students. 5. Ask guiding questions as needed. 6. Have students check if their solutions are reasonable.	**Persevere in Solving the Problem** If students need help, ask: • In the problem, what units is the baby elephant's height given in? (Feet and inches) What unit is used for the heights in the line plot? (Feet only) • How can you convert 4 inches to feet? (Divide 4 by 12) • What is $\frac{4}{12}$ or $\frac{1}{3}$ rounded to the nearest quarter foot? ($\frac{1}{4}$) **SOLUTION** If the height was included, a dot would be added above $2\frac{1}{4}$ feet. Sample answer: Convert 4 inches to feet: $4 \div 12 = \frac{4}{12}$ or $\frac{1}{3}$ foot. Round $\frac{4}{12}$ to the nearest quarter foot: $\frac{4}{12}$ is closer to $\frac{3}{12}$ or $\frac{1}{4}$ than to $\frac{6}{12}$ or $\frac{1}{2}$. So, the elephant's height rounded to the nearest quarter foot is $2\frac{1}{4}$ feet.	**Extra Support** Remind students to divide when converting from a smaller measurement unit to a larger measurement unit. Ask: Is inches a smaller or larger unit than feet? (Smaller) If you convert a measurement from inches to feet, would you divide or multiply? (Divide)
After 7. Discuss the solution. 8. Discuss how to check if the solution is reasonable. 9. Give the problem an extension as needed.	**Check the Answer** Ask: Why is it important to know the number of inches in 1 foot? (You are given the height in feet and inches and want to find the height only in feet.) If students answered that they would add a dot above $2\frac{1}{2}$ feet to the line plot, what mistake did they most likely make? (They probably rounded $2\frac{4}{12}$ to $2\frac{1}{2}$ instead of $2\frac{1}{4}$.)	**Extension** Say: Suppose a baby elephant was born that was 33 inches tall. How would you represent this height on the line plot? Explain. (Convert 33 inches to feet. $33 \div 12 = 2\frac{9}{12}$ or $2\frac{3}{4}$ feet; I would add a dot above $2\frac{3}{4}$ feet.)

Today's Challenge Teacher's Guide

Make a frequency table with the heights of the adult elephants at the reserve. Which height occurred most often? Explain.

Heights (in feet) of Adult Elephants at Reserve (rounded to the nearest half foot)

$10, 11\frac{1}{2}, 13, 10\frac{1}{2}, 12, 12, 9\frac{1}{2},$
$11, 10, 10\frac{1}{2}, 11\frac{1}{2}, 10\frac{1}{2}$

TEACHING ACTIONS	GUIDING QUESTIONS	DIFFERENTIATED INSTRUCTION

Before

1. Read the problem.
2. Ask guiding questions.
3. Discuss possible solution strategies.

Make Sense of the Problem

Help students understand the problem:

- What are you asked to make? (A frequency table with the heights of the adult elephants at the reserve)
- What will you find? (The height that occurred most often)

Vocabulary Review

Have students complete this sentence frame: A table used to record the number of times a value in a data set occurs is called a _____ table. (frequency)

During

4. Observe students.
5. Ask guiding questions as needed.
6. Have students check if their solutions are reasonable.

Persevere in Solving the Problem

If students need help, ask:

- What will you put in the *Tally* column? (Tally marks for each time that height occurs in the data)
- What is the greatest number of times a height occurs? (3)

SOLUTION $10\frac{1}{2}$ feet is the height that occurred most often since it has more tallies than the other heights.

Heights of Adult Elephants

Height (feet)	Tally	Frequency
$9\frac{1}{2}$	I	1
10	II	2
$10\frac{1}{2}$	III	3
11	I	1
$11\frac{1}{2}$	II	2
12	II	2
13	I	1

ELL Support

Explain that *frequency* means "how often something happens." Encourage students to share a sentence about the frequency with which they do something, such as: I have basketball practice 3 times a week. Point out that *3 times a week* tells the frequency with which he or she has basketball practice.

After

7. Discuss the solution.
8. Discuss how to check if the solution is reasonable.
9. Give the problem an extension as needed.

Check the Answer

Ask: How do you know which height occurs most often? (I found the height with the most tally marks.)

To check if their solutions are reasonable, discuss with students why it is important to include a title and labels for the columns of their frequency tables.

Extension

Ask: A baby elephant is $2\frac{1}{2}$ feet tall. How much taller is the tallest adult elephant than the baby elephant? Write an equation to solve. ($10\frac{1}{2}$ feet; $13 - 2\frac{1}{2} = 10\frac{1}{2}$)

Draw a line plot of the heights of the adult elephants at the reserve. How much taller is the tallest elephant than the shortest elephant in inches? Explain.

Heights (in feet) of Adult Elephants at Reserve (rounded to the nearest half foot)

$10, 11\frac{1}{2}, 13, 10\frac{1}{2}, 12, 12, 9\frac{1}{2},$
$11, 10, 10\frac{1}{2}, 11\frac{1}{2}, 10\frac{1}{2}$

TEACHING ACTIONS	GUIDING QUESTIONS	DIFFERENTIATED INSTRUCTION
Before 1. Read the problem. 2. Ask guiding questions. 3. Discuss possible solution strategies.	**Make Sense of the Problem** Help students understand the problem: • What are you asked to draw? (A line plot of the heights of the adult elephants at the reserve) • What are you asked to find? (How much taller the tallest elephant is than the shortest elephant in inches)	
During 4. Observe students. 5. Ask guiding questions as needed. 6. Have students check if their solutions are reasonable.	**Persevere in Solving the Problem** If students need help, ask: • What are the shortest and tallest heights? ($9\frac{1}{2}$ feet; 13 feet) What interval will you use on your number line? ($\frac{1}{2}$ foot) • How will you show the data on your graph? (For each elephant height, I will put a dot above the corresponding number.) • Which unit will you use for your answer? (inches) **SOLUTION** 42 inches taller; Tallest elephant: 13 feet. Shortest elephant: $9\frac{1}{2}$ feet. $13 - 9\frac{1}{2} = 3\frac{1}{2}$. Convert $3\frac{1}{2}$ feet to inches: $\frac{7}{2} \times 12 = \frac{84}{2} = 42$. **Heights of Adult Elephants at Reserve** 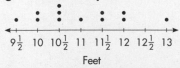 $9\frac{1}{2}$ 10 $10\frac{1}{2}$ 11 $11\frac{1}{2}$ 12 $12\frac{1}{2}$ 13 Feet	**Extra Support** If students have difficulty converting feet to inches, provide these sentence frames for them to complete: 1 foot equals ___ inches. (12) 2 feet equal ___ inches. (24) 3 feet equal ___ inches. (36) Remind students to multiply when converting from a larger measurement unit to a smaller measurement unit.
After 7. Discuss the solution. 8. Discuss how to check if the solution is reasonable. 9. Give the problem an extension as needed.	**Check the Answer** Ask: How many heights should be shown in your line plot? Explain. (12; The number of heights in my line plot should match the number of heights listed in the table.) To check if their solutions are reasonable, ask students to make sure that the difference in height they found is in inches, not in feet.	**Extension** Say: Jared said that most of the elephant heights are greater than 11 feet. Do you agree? Explain. (No; Five of the heights are greater than 11 feet, but 7 of the heights are 11 feet or less.)

Sheila uses the same amount of tomato sauce and tomato paste in each layer. How much of either of these does Sheila put in each layer when she makes 4 layers? Draw a bar diagram and write an equation to show how to find the solution.

Sheila's Vegetarian Lasagna Ingredients (serves 6)

- 3 noodles per layer
- 24 oz spinach
- 15 oz ricotta cheese
- 16 oz mozzarella cheese
- 12 oz parmesan cheese
- 2 eggs
- 32 oz tomato sauce
- 12 oz tomato paste

TEACHING ACTIONS	GUIDING QUESTIONS	DIFFERENTIATED INSTRUCTION
Before 1. Read the problem. 2. Ask guiding questions. 3. Discuss possible solution strategies.	**Make Sense of the Problem** Help students understand the problem: • What are you asked to find? (How much tomato sauce or tomato paste Sheila puts in each layer) • How much tomato sauce is in the lasagna? (32 oz) How much tomato paste? (12 oz) • What else are you asked to do? (Draw a bar diagram and write an equation)	**Vocabulary Review** Review the term *bar diagram*. Discuss how drawing a bar diagram can help students solve this problem.
During 4. Observe students. 5. Ask guiding questions as needed. 6. Have students check if their solutions are reasonable.	**Persevere in Solving the Problem** If students need help, ask: • Sheila divides the tomato sauce and tomato paste into how many equal parts? (4) • For the tomato paste, what expression shows 12 divided into 4 equal parts? ($12 \div 4$) • How can you draw a bar diagram to help answer this question? (Sample answer: My diagram will show that 4 parts are equal to 12 or 32.)	**Extra Support** If students have trouble finding the solution, suggest that they use counters. Have them put 12 or 32 counters on a table to represent the number of ounces. Then have students divide the counters into 4 equal groups.

SOLUTION Sample answer: There are 8 ounces of tomato sauce in each layer; $4 \times s = 32$ or $s = 32 \div 4$; $s = 8$; Sample drawing:

32			
s	s	s	s

After 7. Discuss the solution. 8. Discuss how to check if the solution is reasonable. 9. Give the problem an extension as needed.	**Check the Answer** Ask: How do you know to divide by 4? (Sample answer: Sheila uses the same amount in each layer, and there are 4 layers.) To check if their solutions are reasonable, ask students to multiply their answer by 4. They should arrive at the number of ounces listed in the table for their chosen ingredient.	**Extension** Say: Suppose Sheila puts twice as much spinach in the middle 2 layers as she puts in each of the top and bottom layers. How much spinach does Sheila put in each layer? (Top layer: 4 oz, first middle layer: 8 oz, second middle layer: 8 oz, bottom layer: 4 oz)

 Today's Challenge Teacher's Guide

Sheila has a box of 18 lasagna noodles. She makes a pan of lasagna with 2 layers of noodles. Write and evaluate an expression to find the number of noodles she has left over.

Sheila's Vegetarian Lasagna Ingredients (serves 6)

3 noodles per layer

24 oz spinach

15 oz ricotta cheese

16 oz mozzarella cheese

12 oz parmesan cheese

2 eggs

32 oz tomato sauce

12 oz tomato paste

TEACHING ACTIONS	GUIDING QUESTIONS	DIFFERENTIATED INSTRUCTION
Before 1. Read the problem. 2. Ask guiding questions. 3. Discuss possible solution strategies.	**Make Sense of the Problem** Help students understand the problem: • What does Sheila have? (A box of 18 lasagna noodles) • What does Sheila do? (Makes a pan of lasagna with 2 layers of noodles) • What are you asked to do? (Write and evaluate an expression to find the number of noodles Sheila has left over)	**Vocabulary Review** Review the term *numerical expression*. Discuss the difference between an expression and an equation.
During 4. Observe students. 5. Ask guiding questions as needed. 6. Have students check if their solutions are reasonable.	**Persevere in Solving the Problem** If students need help, ask: • How many noodles per layer does Sheila use? (3) • What operation can you use to find the number of noodles used? (Multiplication) What operation can you use to find the number of noodles left over? (Subtraction) • What does it mean to evaluate an expression? (Sample answer: Find the value that is equal to the expression) **SOLUTION** Sheila has 12 noodles left over; Sample answer: Begin with 18 noodles and subtract 3 noodles for each of the 2 layers. Expression: $18 - (3 \times 2)$; Evaluate: $18 - (3 \times 2) = 18 - 6 = 12$	**ELL Support** Point out to students the root word *value* in the term *evaluate*. To evaluate an expression is to replace the expression with an equivalent value. The equivalent value of the expression $125 + 6$ is 131.
After 7. Discuss the solution. 8. Discuss how to check if the solution is reasonable. 9. Give the problem an extension as needed.	**Check the Answer** Ask: Why is it important to know the order of operations when evaluating an expression? (Sample answer: You will get a different answer if you subtract first rather than multiply first.) Discuss whether students used the correct order of operations. If 30 is given for the answer, students most likely performed the operations from left to right instead of multiplying first.	**Extension** Say: Suppose Sheila is making lasagna with 1 extra noodle on the bottom layer and 1 extra noodle on the top layer. Write and evaluate an expression to find the number of unused noodles. (10 unused noodles; Sample answer: $18 - (3 \times 2) - 2$; $18 - 6 - 2 = 10$)

Sheila has 2 bags of spinach with 15 ounces in each bag. She makes a pan of lasagna with 2 layers of spinach. Write and evaluate an expression for the amount of spinach she has left over. Explain why you did or did not use parentheses.

Sheila's Vegetarian Lasagna Ingredients (serves 6)

3 noodles per layer
24 oz spinach
15 oz ricotta cheese
16 oz mozzarella cheese
12 oz parmesan cheese
2 eggs
32 oz tomato sauce
12 oz tomato paste

TEACHING ACTIONS	GUIDING QUESTIONS	DIFFERENTIATED INSTRUCTION
Before 1. Read the problem. 2. Ask guiding questions. 3. Discuss possible solution strategies.	**Make Sense of the Problem** Help students understand the problem: • What information will you need to use? (Sheila has 2 bags of spinach with 15 ounces in each bag. She uses 24 ounces of spinach.) Is there any extra information? (Yes; The number of layers) • What are you asked to write? (An expression for the ounces of leftover spinach) • What will you explain? (Why I did or did not use parentheses)	**Vocabulary Review** Review the term *parentheses*. Have students evaluate $3 \times (4 - 1)$ with and without parentheses. Discuss whether the results are the same.
During 4. Observe students. 5. Ask guiding questions as needed. 6. Have students check if their solutions are reasonable.	**Persevere in Solving the Problem** If students need help, ask: • What expression can you write to show the total amount of spinach Sheila has? (Sample answer: 2×15) • How can you use the total amount of spinach to find the leftover amount? (Sample answer: Subtract the amount used from the part of the expression for the total amount) • What do parentheses indicate in an expression? (Which operation should be performed first) **SOLUTION** 6 ounces of spinach left over; Sample answer: $2 \times 15 - 24 = 30 - 24 = 6$. I did not need to use parentheses because when using order of operations, I need to multiply before I subtract.	**ELL Support** Make sure all students understand that an ounce is a customary unit of measure. Tell students that 1 ounce is equal to about 28 grams. Remind students that there are 16 ounces in 1 pound.
After 7. Discuss the solution. 8. Discuss how to check if the solution is reasonable. 9. Give the problem an extension as needed.	**Check the Answer** Ask: How many ounces of spinach does Sheila start with? (30 ounces; $2 \times 15 = 30$) To check if their solutions are reasonable, ask students to add the amount of leftover spinach to the amount of spinach used in the lasagna. The total should be equal to the amount of spinach that Sheila has at the start.	**Extension** Say: Suppose Sheila adds 4 more ounces of spinach to the recipe. Write and evaluate an expression for the amount of spinach she has left over. (2 ounces; Sample answer: $(2 \times 15) - (24 + 4) = 30 - 28 = 2$)

Today's Challenge Teacher's Guide

Ken wants to make lasagna to serve 12 people. What rule could Ken apply to Sheila's recipe to determine how much of each ingredient he needs? Use this rule to find the amount of each ingredient that he needs.

Sheila's Vegetarian Lasagna Ingredients (serves 6)	Amount Ken Uses
3 noodles per layer	
24 oz spinach	
15 oz ricotta cheese	
16 oz mozzarella cheese	
12 oz parmesan cheese	
2 eggs	
32 oz tomato sauce	
12 oz tomato paste	

TEACHING ACTIONS	GUIDING QUESTIONS	DIFFERENTIATED INSTRUCTION

Before

1. Read the problem.
2. Ask guiding questions.
3. Discuss possible solution strategies.

Make Sense of the Problem

Help students understand the problem:

- What do you need to find first? (A rule Ken could apply to Sheila's recipe)
- What else are you asked to do? (Use the rule to find the amount of each ingredient he needs.)

During

4. Observe students.
5. Ask guiding questions as needed.
6. Have students check if their solutions are reasonable.

Persevere in Solving the Problem

If students need help, ask:

- How many people does Sheila's recipe serve? (6)
- How much more lasagna does Ken need to make? (Twice as much)

SOLUTION Rule: Multiply the amount of each ingredient Sheila uses by 2. Ken needs twice as much because Ken wants to serve 12 people and Sheila's recipe serves 6 people.

Lasagna Ingredients	Amount Sheila Uses	Amount Ken Uses
noodles per layer	3	6
oz spinach	24	48
oz ricotta cheese	15	30
oz mozzarella cheese	16	32
oz parmesan cheese	12	24
eggs	2	4
oz tomato sauce	32	64
oz tomato paste	12	24

Extra Support

If students have trouble finding a rule that Ken could use, remind them that multiplication is repeated addition. Ken could add two of each of the amounts Sheila uses.

After

7. Discuss the solution.
8. Discuss how to check if the solution is reasonable.
9. Give the problem an extension as needed.

Check the Answer

Ask: What pattern do you see in the completed table? (Sample answer: Every number in the third column is twice the number in the second column.)

To check if their solutions are reasonable, ask students to divide any number in the third column of the table by 2. The answer should be the number in the second column.

Extension

Say: Suppose Ellie is making lasagna for 45 people. What rule could Ellie apply to Sheila's recipe to determine how much of each ingredient she needs? (Multiply each amount by 7.5)

 Today's Challenge Teacher's Guide

Some of the parmesan cheese gets sprinkled on top of the lasagna. The rest gets mixed with the mozzarella and ricotta cheese. Sheila spreads this mixture evenly in 3 layers. Each layer has 13 ounces of the cheese mixture. Write and evaluate an expression to find the amount of parmesan cheese Sheila sprinkles on top of the lasagna.

Sheila's Vegetarian Lasagna Ingredients (serves 6)

- 3 noodles per layer
- 24 oz spinach
- 15 oz ricotta cheese
- 16 oz mozzarella cheese
- 12 oz parmesan cheese
- 2 eggs
- 32 oz tomato sauce
- 12 oz tomato paste

TEACHING ACTIONS	GUIDING QUESTIONS	DIFFERENTIATED INSTRUCTION
Before 1. Read the problem. 2. Ask guiding questions. 3. Discuss possible solution strategies.	**Make Sense of the Problem** Help students understand the problem: • How many ounces of the cheese mixture are in each layer? (13 ounces) • What are you asked to find? (How much parmesan cheese is sprinkled on top) • How will you find the answer? (Write and evaluate an expression)	
During 4. Observe students. 5. Ask guiding questions as needed. 6. Have students check if their solutions are reasonable.	**Persevere in Solving the Problem** If students need help, ask: • How can you find how much cheese is in all of the lasagna? (Sample answer: Find the sum of the ounces of ricotta, mozzarella, and parmesan cheese.) • How can you find how many ounces of cheese are in the layers? (Find 13×3.) • How can you find the amount of parmesan on top of the lasagna? (Subtract the number of ounces of cheese in the 3 layers from the total number of ounces of cheese used.) **SOLUTION** 4 ounces of parmesan cheese are sprinkled on top; Sample answer: $15 + 16 + 12 - 3 \times 13 = 43 - 39 = 4$.	**Extra Support** If students have trouble finding the solution, have them find a partner and discuss what each part of the expression shows. Then have each pair prepare a way to tell what the expression shows using words.
After 7. Discuss the solution. 8. Discuss how to check if the solution is reasonable. 9. Give the problem an extension as needed.	**Check the Answer** Ask: Did you need to use parentheses in your expression? Explain. (Sample answer: No; From left to right, multiplication should be calculated first.) To check if their solutions are reasonable, ask students to complete an equation with $15 + 16 + 12$ on the left side. Ask: What values would you put on the right sides to represent the problem? Use your equation to check your work. (Sample answer: $15 + 16 + 12 = 3 \times 13 + 4$; $43 = 39 + 4$; $43 = 43$)	**Extension** Say: Raaj uses 5 additional ounces of ricotta cheese to make lasagna for 6 people. What expression shows how many ounces of ricotta cheese Raaj needs to serve 60 people? (Sample answer: $10 \times (15 + 5)$)

Today's Challenge Teacher's Guide

What ordered pair names the location for the landing site at point *C*? Explain.

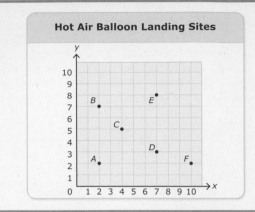

Hot Air Balloon Landing Sites

TEACHING ACTIONS	GUIDING QUESTIONS	DIFFERENTIATED INSTRUCTION
Before 1. Read the problem. 2. Ask guiding questions. 3. Discuss possible solution strategies.	**Make Sense of the Problem** Help students understand the problem: • What are you asked to do? (Name the ordered pair that identifies the location for the landing at point *C*) • What will you use to solve the question? (The graph showing the hot air balloon landing sites)	**Vocabulary Review** Remind students that in an *ordered pair*, there are two numbers, called coordinates. The numbers show the position of *x* (horizontal) and *y* (vertical) values on a graph.
During 4. Observe students. 5. Ask guiding questions as needed. 6. Have students check if their solution is reasonable.	**Persevere in Solving the Problem** If students need help, ask: • Where is the origin? (At (0, 0), where the *x*- and *y*-axes meet. • How can you get to point *C* starting at the origin and moving right first? (Move 4 units to the right along the *x*-axis. Then move up 5 units above the *x*-axis.) • What is the order of the coordinates in an ordered pair? (The *x*-coordinate is first; the *y*-coordinate is second) • What is the ordered pair for point *C*? ((4, 5)) **SOLUTION** (4, 5); Point *C* is located 4 units to the right of the origin (0, 0) along the *x*-axis and 5 units above the *x*-axis. In the ordered pair (4, 5), the *x*-coordinate shows the position to the right of the *y*-axis. The *y*-coordinate shows the position above the *x*-axis.	**ELL Support** Read the problem with students. Explain that the word *landing*, as used in the problem, describes a level place where hot air balloons lift off and return. Have students complete this sentence frame: The balloon came down at the _____ site. (landing)
After 7. Discuss the solution. 8. Discuss how to check if the solution is reasonable. 9. Give the problem an extension as needed.	**Check the Answer** Ask: Why can't you give the answer as (5, 4)? (Sample answer: Because the ordered pair (5, 4) means that the *x*-coordinate is 5 and the *y*-coordinate is 4. The point would be located 5 units to the right of the *y*-axis and 4 units above the *x*-axis.) To check if their solutions are reasonable, ask students to double-check that they counted the units correctly so that they have the correct *x*- and *y*-coordinates.	**Extension** Say: A balloon goes off course and lands 2 units below point *C*. What ordered pair names the location where the balloon landed? ((4, 3))

Today's Challenge Teacher's Guide

A hot air balloon lands at (9, 6). Describe how to graph this ordered pair.

Hot Air Balloon Landing Sites

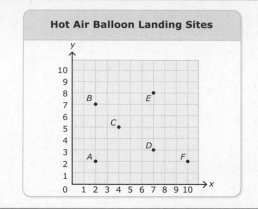

TEACHING ACTIONS	GUIDING QUESTIONS	DIFFERENTIATED INSTRUCTION

Before

1. Read the problem.
2. Ask guiding questions.
3. Discuss possible solution strategies.

Make Sense of the Problem

Help students understand the problem:

- What information do you know from the problem? (A hot air balloon lands at (9, 6).)
- What are you asked to do? (Describe how to graph the ordered pair (9,6).)

Vocabulary Review

Remind students that to graph any point, they need to know its horizontal and vertical distance from (0, 0), or the *origin*.

During

4. Observe students.
5. Ask guiding questions as needed.
6. Have students check if their solution is reasonable.

Persevere in Solving the Problem

If students need help, ask:

- What number in the pair is the *x*-coordinate? (9) How will you use it? (Sample answer: I will start at the origin and move 9 units to the right along the *x*-axis.)
- What number in the pair is the *y*-coordinate? (6) How will you use it? (Sample answer: I will start at the *x*-coordinate, 9, and move up 6 units.)
- Where will you draw a point? (At (9, 6))

SOLUTION Sample answer: Start at the origin. Move 9 units to the right along the *x*-axis. Then move 6 units up. Draw a point and label it (9, 6).

Extra Support

Some students may be confused by the language they need to use when describing how to graph the ordered pair (9, 6). Discuss these simplified steps with students:

1. Start at the origin.
2. Move right 9 units.
3. Move up 6 units.
4. Draw a point and label it (9, 6).

After

7. Discuss the solution.
8. Discuss how to check if the solution is reasonable.
9. Give the problem an extension as needed.

Check the Answer

Ask: Why is it necessary to start at the origin when graphing an ordered pair? (Sample answer: You start with the *x*-coordinate, so you always start at point (0, 0) and move along the *x*-axis.)

To check if their solutions are reasonable, ask students to read their descriptions to a partner. Tell them that their descriptions are like maps for their partners to follow. Without a good description, the partners will not be able to find where the balloon lands.

Extension

Say: Another hot air balloon lands at (10, 7). Describe how to graph this ordered pair. (Sample answer: Start at the origin and move 10 units to the right along the *x*-axis. Then move 7 units up. Draw a point and label it (10, 7).)

 Today's Challenge Teacher's Guide

A hot air balloon lands 3 units to the right of point *A*. What are the coordinates of the balloon's landing site? Explain.

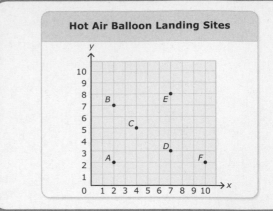

Hot Air Balloon Landing Sites

TEACHING ACTIONS	GUIDING QUESTIONS	DIFFERENTIATED INSTRUCTION
Before 1. Read the problem. 2. Ask guiding questions. 3. Discuss possible solution strategies.	**Make Sense of the Problem** Help students understand the problem: • What are you asked to do? (Tell the coordinates of the balloon's landing site) • Where did the balloon land? (3 units to the right of point *A*)	
During 4. Observe students. 5. Ask guiding questions as needed. 6. Have students check if their solution is reasonable.	**Persevere in Solving the Problem** If students need help, ask: • What is the *x*-coordinate for point *A*? (2) What is the *y*-coordinate for point *A*? (2) • What ordered pair names the location for point *A*? ((2, 2)) • What happens to the *x*-coordinate when you move 3 units to its right along the *x*-axis? (It increases by 3 to become 5.) Does the *y*-coordinate change? (No) So, what are the coordinates of the balloon's landing site? ((5, 2)) **SOLUTION** (5, 2); Sample answer: The location of point *A* is (2, 2). Moving 3 units to the right of point *A* increases the *x*-coordinate by 3. So, the coordinates of the landing site are (5, 2).	**ELL Support** To help students better understand graphing terms, post a list of the following: *axes, graph, ordered pair, origin, x-axis, x-coordinate, y-axis, y-coordinate, ordered pair*. Review each word and definition with students, showing examples on a graph.
After 7. Discuss the solution. 8. Discuss how to check if the solution is reasonable. 9. Give the problem an extension as needed.	**Check the Answer** Ask: Why didn't you change the *y*-coordinate? (Sample answer: Because the balloon landed 3 units to the right of point *A*, so only the *x*-coordinate changes. The *y*-coordinate stays the same.) To check if their solutions are reasonable, ask: To find the new coordinates, did you count 3 units to the right along the *x*-axis? (Yes)	**Extension** Ask: If the balloon lands 5 units up from point *A*, which point on the graph names its landing site? What are the coordinates? (Point *B*; The coordinates are (2, 7))

Today's Challenge Teacher's Guide

Tom's hot air balloon landed at point *D*. Mariah's hot air balloon landed at point *E*. What is the vertical distance between their landing sites? Explain.

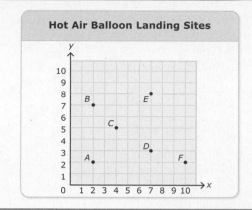

Hot Air Balloon Landing Sites

TEACHING ACTIONS	GUIDING QUESTIONS	DIFFERENTIATED INSTRUCTION

Before

1. Read the problem.
2. Ask guiding questions.
3. Discuss possible solution strategies.

Make Sense of the Problem

Help students understand the problem:

- Which points on the graph will you need to look at for this problem? (points *D* and *E*)
- What are you asked to do to solve the problem? (Find the vertical distance between points *D* and *E*)
- Why is it important to explain your answer? (Sample answer: So that it is clear I understand my answer.)

Vocabulary Review

Draw students' attention to points *D* and *E* on the graph. Have students trace the *vertical distance* between the two points. Show them how this vertical distance is parallel to the *y*-axis.

During

4. Observe students.
5. Ask guiding questions as needed.
6. Have students check if their solution is reasonable.

Persevere in Solving the Problem

If students need help, ask:

- What are the coordinates for point *D*? ((7, 3))
- What are the coordinates for point *E*? ((7, 8))
- Which coordinate is the same for each point? (The *x*-coordinate) Which is different? (The *y*-coordinate) How will you find the difference between the *y*-coordinates? (Subtract)

SOLUTION 5 units; Sample answer: The coordinates for point *D* are (7, 3). The coordinates for point *E* are (7, 8). Both points have the same *x*-coordinate. The difference between their *y*-coordinates is the vertical distance: $8 - 3 = 5$.

ELL Support

Review the terms *vertical* and *horizontal* with students. For kinesthetic learner support, have students raise both arms straight up and say *vertical*, and then stretch both arms out to the sides and say *horizontal*. Repeat.

After

7. Discuss the solution.
8. Discuss how to check if the solution is reasonable.
9. Give the problem an extension as needed.

Check the Answer

Ask: Can you find the answer without subtracting? (Sample answer: Yes; I can count the number of units on the grid from point *D* to point *E* to find the vertical distance.)

To check if their solutions are reasonable, ask students: Did you use subtraction to find the vertical distance? (Yes) How can you use addition to check your answer? (Sample answer: I can add: $5 + 3 = 8$.)

Extension

Say: Tom's hot air balloon landed at point *A* and Mariah's hot air balloon landed at point *B*. Is the vertical distance between these points different from the vertical distance between points *D* and *E*? (No; The vertical distance between both pairs of points is 5 units.)

Today's Challenge Teacher's Guide

The Clark family's hot air balloon lands so its coordinates form a rectangle with point *A*, point *B*, and point *F*. What are the coordinates of the balloon's landing site? Explain how you know.

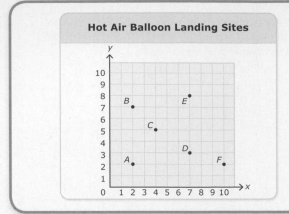

Hot Air Balloon Landing Sites

TEACHING ACTIONS	GUIDING QUESTIONS	DIFFERENTIATED INSTRUCTION
Before 1. Read the problem. 2. Ask guiding questions. 3. Discuss possible solution strategies.	**Make Sense of the Problem** Help students understand the problem: • What do you know about the landing site for the Clark family's balloon? (Its location forms a rectangle with three other points, *A*, *B*, and *F*.) • What do you need to find? (The coordinates of the landing site)	**Vocabulary Review** Review with students that a rectangle is a quadrilateral with four right angles and four sides whose opposite sides are equal in length and parallel.
During 4. Observe students. 5. Ask guiding questions as needed. 6. Have students check if their solution is reasonable.	**Persevere in Solving the Problem** If students need help, ask: • What do you know about a rectangle that can help you solve this problem? (Sample answer: A rectangle is a quadrilateral with two pairs of parallel sides and four right angles.) • Which points can you connect to form two of the sides of the rectangle? (Point *B* to point *A* and point *A* to point *F*.) • How can you describe the location of the landing site? (It is 10 units to the right of the origin and 7 units above it.) **SOLUTION** (10, 7); Sample answer: The landing site is the fourth vertex in the rectangle. It has the same *x*-coordinate as point *F* (10, 2) and the same *y*-coordinate as point *B* (2, 7). So, the location is at (10, 7).	**Extra Support** If students have trouble finding the solution, draw the same points in a coordinate graph. Connect the given points so that students can better visualize how the rectangle can be formed. Make sure they understand that the fourth vertex must be at (10, 7) to form a right angle.
After 7. Discuss the solution. 8. Discuss how to check if the solution is reasonable. 9. Give the problem an extension as needed.	**Check the Answer** Ask: Why aren't the coordinates for point *A* used to help determine the *x*- and *y*-coordinates for the new landing site? (Sample answer: Because the new landing site is above point *F* and to the right of point *B*.) To check if their solutions are reasonable, ask the following questions: If the four points were connected, would there be four sides? (Yes) Would opposite sides be equal in length and parallel? (Yes) Are there four right angles? (Yes)	**Extension** Say: A balloon lands at a point 2 units to the left of (10, 2). Does this landing site still form a rectangle with points *A*, *B*, and *F*? Explain. (No; Sample answer: When connected to the other points, the coordinates for the new landing site do not create a rectangle.)

 Today's Challenge Teacher's Guide

Miranda drew a graph showing the distance of the football from the quarterback after each second. What does the point (3, 30) represent on her graph?

Position of Football and Receiver

Time After Quarterback Throws (seconds)	Distance of Football from Quarterback (yards)	Distance of Receiver from Quarterback (yards)
0	0	45
1	10	46
2	20	47
3	30	48
4	40	49
5	50	50

TEACHING ACTIONS	GUIDING QUESTIONS	DIFFERENTIATED INSTRUCTION

Before

1. Read the problem.
2. Ask guiding questions.
3. Discuss possible solution strategies.

Make Sense of the Problem

Help students understand the problem:

- What does the table show? (The position of the football and receiver)
- What does Miranda's graph show? (The distance of the football from the quarterback after each second)
- What are you asked to tell? (What the point (3, 30) represents on her graph)

Vocabulary Review

Review the term *ordered pair*. Show a coordinate grid and ask students to locate and graph several sets of ordered pairs.

During

4. Observe students.
5. Ask guiding questions as needed.
6. Have students check if their solutions are reasonable.

Persevere in Solving the Problem

If students need help, ask:

- In an ordered pair, which coordinate is first? (The x-coordinate)
- On Miranda's graph, what does the x-coordinate represent? (The number of seconds after the quarterback throws) What does the y-coordinate represent? (The number of yards the football is from the quarterback)

SOLUTION After 3 seconds, the football is 30 yards away from the quarterback. The x-coordinate represents the number of seconds after the quarterback throws. The y-coordinate represents the number of yards the football is from the quarterback.

ELL Support

Make sure students understand the basics of American football so that they can understand the information in the table. Tell students that the *quarterback* is the player who throws the football to start a passing play. At 0 seconds, the football is with the quarterback because it has not been thrown yet.

After

7. Discuss the solution.
8. Discuss how to check if the solution is reasonable.
9. Give the problem an extension as needed.

Check the Answer

Ask: Will 3 seconds be to the left or right of 2 seconds on the graph? Why? (Sample answer: To the right, because time increases as you move to the right)

To check if their solutions are reasonable, ask students what the values of the ordered pair represent. Ask: Which unit of measurement does the 3 represent? (Seconds) The 30? (Yards)

Extension

Ask: In Miranda's graph, what is the ordered pair for the point at 4 seconds after the quarterback throws the football? (4, 40)

Today's Challenge Teacher's Guide

Carlos drew a graph showing the distance of the receiver from the quarterback after each second. What does the point (2, 47) represent on his graph?

Position of Football and Receiver

Time After Quarterback Throws (seconds)	Distance of Football from Quarterback (yards)	Distance of Receiver from Quarterback (yards)
0	0	45
1	10	46
2	20	47
3	30	48
4	40	49
5	50	50

TEACHING ACTIONS	GUIDING QUESTIONS	DIFFERENTIATED INSTRUCTION

Before

1. Read the problem.
2. Ask guiding questions.
3. Discuss possible solution strategies.

Make Sense of the Problem

Help students understand the problem:

- What does Carlos's graph show? (The distance of the receiver from the quarterback after each second)
- What are you asked to describe? (What the point (2, 47) represents on his graph)
- Where can you find the distance the receiver is from the quarterback after each second? (The third column of the table)

During

4. Observe students.
5. Ask guiding questions as needed.
6. Have students check if their solutions are reasonable.

Persevere in Solving the Problem

If students need help, ask:

- What does the x-coordinate of an ordered pair indicate? (The number of units to move from the origin along the x-axis)
- In Carlos's graph, what what does the x-coordinate represent? (The number of seconds after the quarterback throws) What does the y-coordinate represent? (The number of yards the receiver is from the quarterback)

SOLUTION After 2 seconds, the receiver is 47 yards away from the quarterback. The x-coordinate represents the number of seconds after the quarterback throws. The y-coordinate represents the number of yards the receiver is from the quarterback.

Extra Support

If students have trouble finding the solution, encourage them to use a coordinate grid and a coin or counter to model graphing ordered pairs. Have them slide the coin or counter x units to the right and y units up.

After

7. Discuss the solution.
8. Discuss how to check if the solution is reasonable.
9. Give the problem an extension as needed.

Check the Answer

Ask: How did you use the information in the table? (Sample answer: I used the headings in the columns to understand that 2 is the time in seconds and 47 is the distance in yards that the receiver is from the quarterback.)

Discuss whether students answered the right question. If students describe how far away the football is from the quarterback, they used the data in the second column instead of the data in the third column.

Extension

Ask: What is the first ordered pair in the graph Carlos drew? What does the point represent? ((0, 45); Sample answer: The receiver is 45 yards from the quarterback when the quarterback first has the ball.)

Describe a pattern you see in the numbers in the first and second columns of the table.

| Position of Football and Receiver | | |
Time After Quarterback Throws (seconds)	Distance of Football from Quarterback (yards)	Distance of Receiver from Quarterback (yards)
0	0	45
1	10	46
2	20	47
3	30	48
4	40	49
5	50	50

TEACHING ACTIONS	GUIDING QUESTIONS	DIFFERENTIATED INSTRUCTION

Before

1. Read the problem.
2. Ask guiding questions.
3. Discuss possible solution strategies.

Make Sense of the Problem

Help students understand the problem:

- What are you asked to do? (Describe a pattern in the the numbers in the first and second columns of the table.)
- What information is in the first column? (Time after the quarterback throws, in seconds)
- What information is in the second column? (Distance of football from quarterback, in yards)

During

4. Observe students.
5. Ask guiding questions as needed.
6. Have students check if their solutions are reasonable.

Persevere in Solving the Problem

If students need help, ask:

- How do the numbers in the first column change as you move down? (Sample answer: They increase by 1.)
- How do the numbers in the second column change as you move down? (Sample answer: They increase by 10.)
- How is each number in the second column related to its corresponding number in the first column? (Sample answer: Each number is 10 times its corresponding number.)

SOLUTION Sample answer: Each number in the second column is 10 times its corresponding number in the first column. $1 \times 10 = 10$, $2 \times 10 = 20$, and so on.

ELL Support

Review the term *pattern* as a repeating sequence of numbers that follows a rule. Help students identify the pattern rule within the first column (+1) and within the second column (+10). Point out that they need to find a pattern rule that describes how the numbers in the first column relate to the numbers in the second column.

After

7. Discuss the solution.
8. Discuss how to check if the solution is reasonable.
9. Give the problem an extension as needed.

Check the Answer

Ask: Why should you use more than one row in the table to look for a pattern? (If you just look at the second row of numbers, you might think the rule is to add 9 to the number in the first column.)

To check if their answers are reasonable, ask students to divide each number in the second column by 10. The quotient should be the number in the first column.

Extension

Say: In another game, the football is 27 yards from the quarterback after 3 seconds, 36 yards from the quarterback after 4 seconds, and 45 yards from the quarterback after 5 seconds. What is a rule for the pattern? (Multiply the number of seconds by 9.)

 Today's Challenge Teacher's Guide

Graph the data in the table representing the distance of the football from the quarterback after each second. Let the numbers in the first column represent the *x*-coordinates and the numbers in the second column represent the *y*-coordinates.

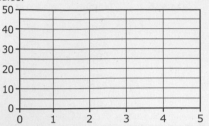

Position of Football and Receiver

Time After Quarterback Throws (seconds)	Distance of Football from Quarterback (yards)	Distance of Receiver from Quarterback (yards)
0	0	45
1	10	46
2	20	47
3	30	48
4	40	49
5	50	50

TEACHING ACTIONS	GUIDING QUESTIONS	DIFFERENTIATED INSTRUCTION

Before

1. Read the problem.
2. Ask guiding questions.
3. Discuss possible solution strategies.

Make Sense of the Problem

Help students understand the problem:

- What are you asked to graph? (The distance of the football from the quarterback after each second)
- What type of graph will you draw? (A line graph) Where will you draw it? (On the coordinate grid provided)
- What columns from the table will you use? (The first and second columns)

Vocabulary Review

Review the term *line graph* with students. Explain that a line graph connects points to show how data change over time. Tell students that they should connect the points they have plotted in the graph.

During

4. Observe students.
5. Ask guiding questions as needed.
6. Have students check if their solutions are reasonable.

Persevere in Solving the Problem

If students need help, ask:

- How will you label the *x*-axis? (Sample answer: Seconds after Throw)
- To graph the data in the first row of the table, what ordered pair will you use? (0, 0)
- How will you plot (2, 20)? (Sample answer: Begin at the origin and move 2 units to the right and then 20 units up.)

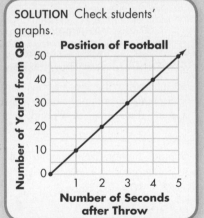

SOLUTION Check students' graphs.

Extra Support

Point out to students that each row in the table represents an ordered pair for a point on the graph. Ask: How many points will be on your graph? (6) What ordered pairs will you graph? ((0, 0), (1, 10), (2, 20), (3, 30), (4, 40), (5, 50))

After

7. Discuss the solution.
8. Discuss how to check if the solution is reasonable.
9. Give the problem an extension as needed.

Check the Answer

Ask: Why is it important to begin your graph at the origin? (Sample answer: The origin is the point (0, 0), and the data starts at 0 seconds and 0 yards)

Discuss whether students graphed each ordered pair correctly. Remind them to check that they connected the points with a line to complete their graphs.

Extension

Say: Look at your graph. What is the relationship between the number of yards the football is from the quarterback and the number of seconds after the quarterback throws? (The number of yards is 10 times the number of seconds.)

Graph the data in the table representing the distance of the receiver from the quarterback after each second. Do you notice a pattern in your graph? Explain.

Position of Football and Receiver

Time After Quarterback Throws (seconds)	Distance of Football from Quarterback (yards)	Distance of Receiver from Quarterback (yards)
0	0	45
1	10	46
2	20	47
3	30	48
4	40	49
5	50	50

TEACHING ACTIONS	GUIDING QUESTIONS	DIFFERENTIATED INSTRUCTION
Before 1. Read the problem. 2. Ask guiding questions. 3. Discuss possible solution strategies.	**Make Sense of the Problem** Help students understand the problem: • What should your graph show? (The distance of the receiver from the quarterback after each second) What type of graph will you draw? (A line graph) • Where can you find the distance of the receiver from the quarterback? (In the third column of the table)	
During 4. Observe students. 5. Ask guiding questions as needed. 6. Have students check if their solutions are reasonable.	**Persevere in Solving the Problem** If students need help, ask: • Where will the graph begin? (At (0, 45)) • What pattern do you see in the first and third columns of the table? (Sample answer: As you go from one row to the next, both numbers increase by 1.) **SOLUTION** Yes; As time increases by 1 second, distance increases by 1 yard. 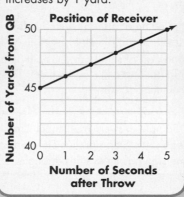	**Extra Support** If students have trouble finding the solution, encourage them to make a list of just the *y*-coordinates. Have students look for a pattern in the numbers. Ask whether the numbers go from one to the next by adding or by multiplying. (By adding)
After 7. Discuss the solution. 8. Discuss how to check if the solution is reasonable. 9. Give the problem an extension as needed.	**Check the Answer** Ask: What is a rule for the pattern? (Sample answer: Add 1 to the *x*-coordinate and add 1 to the *y*-coordinate) To check if their solutions are reasonable, ask students to find two points that they have plotted. For each point, have them look at the axes to find the *x*- and *y*-coordinates. Then have them check to see that the coordinates match the ordered pair in the table.	**Extension** Ask: After 9 seconds, what do you think the distance of the receiver from the quarterback would be? (54 yards from the quarterback)

Classify 3 signs by the number of sides they have. Do not include any 2 that have the same number of sides.

TEACHING ACTIONS	GUIDING QUESTIONS	DIFFERENTIATED INSTRUCTION
Before 1. Read the problem. 2. Ask guiding questions. 3. Discuss possible solution strategies.	**Make Sense of the Problem** Help students understand the problem: • What do the pictures show? (6 road signs) • What are you asked to do? (Classify 3 signs by the number of sides they have) • Which signs should NOT be included? (Any two signs with the same number of sides)	**Vocabulary Review** Remind students that a *pentagon* is a 5 sided-polygon and an *octagon* is an 8-sided polygon.
During 4. Observe students. 5. Ask guiding questions as needed. 6. Have students check if their solutions are reasonable.	**Persevere in Solving the Problem** If students need help, ask: • What does it mean to classify the signs by the number of sides they have? (Name the shapes according to their number of sides) • What is the name of a shape with 3 sides? (Triangle) With 5 sides? (Pentagon) With eight sides? (Octagon) • What is one pair of signs that you cannot include? (Sample answer: No Parking and Do Not Enter; This pair of signs has the same number of sides.) **SOLUTION** Sample answer: The School Crossing sign has five sides: pentagon; the Stop sign has eight sides: octagon; the No Passing Zone sign has three sides: triangle.	**ELL Support** Make sure all students know that a *quadrilateral* is a shape with 4 sides. To help students remember the term, tell them that *quad* means "four." Have students complete and say this sentence frame: A shape with 4 sides is called a _____. (quadrilateral)
After 7. Discuss the solution. 8. Discuss how to check if the solution is reasonable. 9. Give the problem an extension as needed.	**Check the Answer** Ask: How many different shapes are shown? Explain (4; There are 1 pentagon, 1 octagon, 2 triangles, and 2 quadrilaterals.) Disucss with students if their solutions are reasonable. If hexagon is given for an answer, students named a 6-sided shape. However, none of the signs has 6 sides.	**Extension** Ask: What 2 shapes could you put together to make a pentagon? Explain. (Sample answer: A triangle and a quadrilateral; Place a quadrilateral and a triangle together so that they have a common side.)

 Today's Challenge Teacher's Guide

Which signs are triangles? Classify each triangle in as many ways as possible.

TEACHING ACTIONS	GUIDING QUESTIONS	DIFFERENTIATED INSTRUCTION

Before

1. Read the problem.
2. Ask guiding questions.
3. Discuss possible solution strategies.

Make Sense of the Problem

Help students understand the problem:

- What are you asked to name? (The signs that are triangles)
- What else are you asked to do? (Classify each triangle in as many ways as possible)

Vocabulary Review

Review the definitions of *right triangle*, *acute triangle*, *obtuse triangle*, and *equilateral triangle*. Ask students to draw an example of each type.

During

4. Observe students.
5. Ask guiding questions as needed.
6. Have students check if their solutions are reasonable.

Persevere in Solving the Problem

If students need help, ask:

- What is one sign that is a triangle? (Sample answer: No Passing Zone sign)
- What are two ways you can classify a triangle? (Sample answer: By the lengths of the sides; by the measures of the angles)
- What is an isosceles triangle? (A triangle that has 2 sides that are the same length)

> **SOLUTION** The Yield sign and the No Passing Zone sign; The Yield sign is an equilateral and acute triangle. All of its sides are the same length and all of its angles are acute; The No Passing Zone sign is an isosceles and acute triangle. Two of its sides are the same length and all of its angles are acute

ELL Support

To help students understand the word *classify*, tell them that it means "to sort things into classes or groups." You might *classify* movies by genre—comedy, drama, action, science fiction, and so on. Remind students that all items in a class or group should have at least one attribute in common.

After

7. Discuss the solution.
8. Discuss how to check if the solution is reasonable.
9. Give the problem an extension as needed.

Check the Answer

Ask: How can you tell if an angle is acute? (Sample answer: The angle measure is less than 90°, or smaller than the angle made by the corner of a piece of paper.)

To check if their solutions are reasonable, ask students to make sure they looked at the lengths of the sides and the size of the angles when classifying their triangles.

Extension

Say: Suppose the School Crossing sign is divided into a triangle and a rectangle. Classify the triangle in as many ways as possible. (Sample answer: Isosceles and right triangle)

Today's Challenge Teacher's Guide

Name all the polygons that can be used to describe the No Parking sign. Explain why each shape fits the sign.

TEACHING ACTIONS	GUIDING QUESTIONS	DIFFERENTIATED INSTRUCTION
Before 1. Read the problem. 2. Ask guiding questions. 3. Discuss possible solution strategies.	**Make Sense of the Problem** Help students understand the problem: • What are you asked to name? (All of the polygons that can be used to describe the No Parking sign) • What else are you asked to do? (Explain why each shape fits the sign)	
During 4. Observe students. 5. Ask guiding questions as needed. 6. Have students check if their solutions are reasonable.	**Persevere in Solving the Problem** If students need help, ask: • How many sides does the No Parking sign have? (4) • How do you classify the shape by the number of its sides? (Quadrilateral) • What else do you notice about the No Parking sign? (Sample answer: Opposite sides are parallel; opposite sides are the same length; there are 4 right angles.) **SOLUTION** Quadrilateral, because it has 4 sides; Parallelogram, because opposite sides are parallel and equal in length; Rectangle, because there are 4 right angles.	**Extra Support** If students have trouble finding the solution, encourage them to make a list of possible names for shapes that have 4 sides. Then have them check whether or not the No Parking sign fits the definition for each name.
After 7. Discuss the solution. 8. Discuss how to check if the solution is reasonable. 9. Give the problem an extension as needed.	**Check the Answer** Ask: Why is it important to look at both the side lengths and the angle measures of the No Parking sign? (Sample answer: A parallelogram has opposite sides that are parallel and the same length, and a rectangle also has 4 right angles.) To check if their solutions are reasonable, ask students if they named 3 different polygons. If they only named 2, ask them to think of another name that also describes the No Parking sign.	**Extension** Ask: What polygon has 2 fewer sides than a hexagon, no acute angles, and 4 sides that are all the same length? (A square)

Today's Challenge Teacher's Guide

Regular polygons have all angles equal in measure and all sides equal in length. Which of the signs are regular polygons? Explain.

TEACHING ACTIONS	GUIDING QUESTIONS	DIFFERENTIATED INSTRUCTION
Before 1. Read the problem. 2. Ask guiding questions. 3. Discuss possible solution strategies.	**Make Sense of the Problem** Help students understand the problem: • What are you asked to find? (The signs that are regular polygons) • What else are you asked to do? (Explain my answer)	**Vocabulary Review** Review the definition of *rhombus*. Ask students for the name of a rhombus with 4 right angles. (A square)
During 4. Observe students. 5. Ask guiding questions as needed. 6. Have students check if their solutions are reasonable.	**Persevere in Solving the Problem** If students need help, ask: • What is a regular polygon? (A polygon with all angles equal in measure and all sides equal in length) • What is an example of a regular polygon? (Sample answer: A square) • What is one sign with all sides of equal length? (Sample answer: The Yield sign) Can you see that all of the angles are also equal in measure? (Yes) **SOLUTION** 3 signs are regular polygons: Yield, Stop, and Do Not Enter; In each sign, all the angles are the same measure and all the sides are equal in length.	**Extra Support** If students have trouble finding the solution, suggest they use a ruler to measure the lengths of the sides for each sign. Ask them to name the signs that do and do not have all sides of equal length.
After 7. Discuss the solution. 8. Discuss how to check if the solution is reasonable. 9. Give the problem an extension as needed.	**Check the Answer** Ask: Is it important to count the number of sides? Why or why not? (No; a regular polygon can have any number of sides.) To check if their solutions are reasonable, ask: How do you know that the No Parking sign is not a regular polygon? (Sample answer: Even though all of its angles are equal in measure, Its sides are not all the same length.)	**Extension** Ask: What is another name for a regular polygon with 5 fewer angles than an octagon? (An equilateral triangle)

Today's Challenge Teacher's Guide

If the Stop sign has a perimeter of 96 inches, find the length of each side. Explain how to find the answer, including telling what kind of polygon the Stop sign is.

TEACHING ACTIONS	GUIDING QUESTIONS	DIFFERENTIATED INSTRUCTION
Before 1. Read the problem. 2. Ask guiding questions. 3. Discuss possible solution strategies.	**Make Sense of the Problem** Help students understand the problem: • What information are you given? (The Stop sign has a perimeter of 96 inches.) • What are you asked to find? (The length of each side) • What else are you asked to tell? (The type of polygon it is and how to find the answer)	
During 4. Observe students. 5. Ask guiding questions as needed. 6. Have students check if their solutions are reasonable.	**Persevere in Solving the Problem** If students need help, ask: • What is the perimeter of a figure? (The distance around it) • How many sides does the Stop sign have? (8) • What is this shape called? (An octagon) • If it is 96 inches all the way around the Stop sign, what operation can you use to find the length of one side? (Sample answer: Division) What equation can you write to solve the problem? (Sample equation: $96 \div 8 = n$) **SOLUTION** Each side is 12 inches long. Divide the perimeter by 8: $96 \div 8 = 12$. A Stop sign is a regular octagon because it has 8 sides of equal length and 8 angles of equal measure.	**Extra Support** If students have trouble finding the solution, encourage them to make a table of shapes. Have them include a picture of the shape, the number of sides, the name of the shape, and at least one example of an object with that shape.
After 7. Discuss the solution. 8. Discuss how to check if the solution is reasonable. 9. Give the problem an extension as needed.	**Check the Answer** Ask: How can you find the length of one side of a regular polygon if you know the perimeter? (Divide the perimeter by the number of sides) To check if their solutions are reasonable, ask students to multiply their answer by 8. The product should be equal to the perimeter, 96 inches.	**Extension** Say: Suppose the No Parking sign is twice as tall as it is wide. If the perimeter of the sign is 54 inches, how long is each side? (Short sides: 9 inches; long sides: 18 inches)

Today's Challenge Teacher's Guide